Borderline Personality Disorder

Struggling Understanding Succeeding

Colleen E. Warner, PsyD

PESI HEALTHCARE, LLC
PO Box 1000
200 Spring Street
Eau Claire, Wisconsin 54702

Printed in the United States of America

ISBN: 0-9749711-0-3

Acknowledgments

I wish to express my deepest gratitude to the colleagues, friends, and family who have supported me in this and many other endeavors. Thank you to Michael Olson and PESI Healthcare for having the faith in me to pursue this work. Thanks to Dr. Christopher Babbitt and the Staff of Northwest Counseling in New Richmond, Wisconsin for their flexibility and support. Special appreciation to the Cumberland Memorial Library Staff for their assistance in obtaining reference materials.

Not a word would have been written without the encouragement and support of dear friends and colleagues Cindy O'Keefe and Karen Kaufman. Thank you to Lydia Vitort of Systemic Solutions LLC for keeping me realistic and on task. Most of all for being a good friend in the process. During the writing process I was supplied with encouragement and great coffee from the Women's Entrepreneurs Group and Railway Espresso of Spooner, Wisconsin. Finally, thank you to my life partner, Michael, who makes me feel like I can do anything, (but I don't have to!) and to our children who make me laugh and remind me what is most important.

About the Author

Dr. Colleen Warner is a licensed psychologist in the state of Wisconsin and a member of the National Registry of Health Services Providers in Psychology. She holds a Bachelors of Music Education in Music Therapy from the University of Kansas and completed her Doctorate of Psychology at the Minnesota School of Professional Psychology *(Argosy University).*

Dr. Warner provides training nationally for PESI Healthcare on the topic of Borderline Personality Disorder. Her years of experience, passion, and empathy combined with her "down to earth" presentation style and sense of humor have been appreciated by professionals across the country. She draws on her experience as a supervisor in rural mental health clinics where her caseload often consisted of the most difficult to treat clients, including those with Borderline Personality Disorder. Dr. Warner provides supervision and consultation to other practitioners struggling with the challenges of treating Borderlines and thus, has developed an understanding of the health care provider's frustration elicited by these difficult cases.

Currently in private practice, Dr. Warner continues to have an interest in clients with Borderline Personality Disorder and other Co-Morbid conditions. Dr. Warner also conducts training in the areas of Suicide Prevention, Crisis Management, Dealing with Difficult Patient Behavior, and Mental Health Topics for School and Medical Professionals.

Dr. Warner is available for consultation and as a presenter on a variety of topics at: drcolleen@charter.net.

Table of Contents

Preface

While clients with Borderline Personality Disorder (BPD) are thought to be some of the most difficult to work with, clinicians with the least experience and training often wind up with a disproportionate number of borderlines on their caseloads. More experienced clinicians set limits on the number of Borderlines on their caseload, while naïve and eager new professionals take them on. In addition, these demanding clients often fill inpatient units, group homes, and case management programs where staff providing the bulk of direct services may have minimal experience or training in dealing with the complexities of BPD.

Like so many novices I eagerly took on Borderline clients with minimal understanding of their complexities. I entered the mental health field thinking that if I just cared enough I could somehow be more effective with clients than my predecessors. The problem was simply that other clinicians were not motivated or dedicated enough or were "too judgmental." How ironic it is now to see that it was I that was being judgmental! It's hard to admit I was ever this naïve and arrogant, but I doubt I am the first (or last) clinician to have such grandiose and self-important fantasies.

My ideals of "caring enough" were most quickly shot down in working with my first client with Borderline Personality Disorder. No amount of caring could ameliorate her self-abusive patterns and if anything, at times, my empathy seemed to make it worse. What I needed was not "empathy," it was skills. What she needed was not "caring," it was skills.

At the time, the field didn't offer much help. Training in dealing with Borderlines was minimal and many people considered Borderline clients "untreatable." This thinking was particularly unhelpful in inpatient and community mental health settings where chronic struggles with self injury and repeat hospitalizations forced the community to "try something" to help these clients. The "psychobabble" of the analytic theories was confusing to me at best and even when I could understand it, I was left wondering "Okay, but what do I *do?*"

As a result, the skills I did develop were mostly a result of trial and error experience and good advice from experienced clinicians with good instincts. Unfortunately, even the skills I learned in terms of "setting boundaries" and "avoiding manipulation" seemed to backfire at times. I felt like I was "experimenting" on each client. I was usually left feeling incompetent. I needed a better way of understanding these people and I needed to know what skill to use when.

Answers began to come in graduate school when we were required to read Marsha Linehan's pivotal book *Cognitive Behavioral Therapy for Borderline Personality Disorder.* Finally, a theory that made sense to me and wasn't so judgmental. I was eager to put it into practice. Unfortunately, in the rural community mental health center where I worked, the resources to do a full DBT program didn't exist. Furthermore, I was one of very few providers who had even heard of DBT. Nonetheless I began applying the principles to the best of my ability and found that even if they didn't always seem to work, at least I found myself less frustrated!

A new struggle came when I was promoted to supervisor. Now not only was I supposed to help the client, but it was my role to help the clinician as well. How could I share what I had learned, especially with seasoned clinicians who had years of experience on me, and had developed an attitude of "I don't do Borderlines!"

I had to start at the beginning. I had to change attitudes. I had to take Linehan's useful but dense and intensive work and break it down into simple and brief steps that could be presented in a few minutes at staffing. I needed to do it in an understandable and down to earth language that clinicians could understand and remember. Most importantly I needed to be patient. Like the work with Borderline clients, change would happen but it would be slow and tedious.

This book is both a result of and part of that change. It is intended to be a resource to both clinicians with experience and new comers to the field. It is a humble attempt to share experiences, knowledge, and most importantly, attitudes that I have found useful in treating clients with this disorder. More than anything it is an attempt to give providers a way of understanding Borderlines that will make the work less frustrating and with any luck, more effective.

Finally, it is a tribute to those clients who have been willing to work with me. For as difficult as this disorder may be for clinicians it is even more difficult to live with it twenty-four hours a day. The clients I have known with BPD are amongst the strongest, bravest, most resourceful and creative people I've known, and it has been honor to share with them their struggles and successes.

AUTHOR'S NOTE

The clients described in this book are composites based on the author's experience. Every effort has been made to conceal the actual identities of clients. Any similarities between these descriptions and actual individuals is purely coincidental and likely a result of the commonalities of experiences these clients share.

1

The Struggle: Living with Borderline Personality Disorder

THE PROVIDER'S STRUGGLE

> *"I left graduate school naïve and full of empathy . . . I knew I'd met my first Borderline when I had the urge to strap her to a nuclear rocket and ship her straight to the moon."*

> *"I enjoyed your conference immensely, but will still refer borderlines out. I have practiced 25 years and find them to be extremely difficult and dangerous."*

The above comments by providers of human services illustrate the frustration, fear, and avoidance elicited by clients with Borderline Personality Disorder (BPD). As I travel conducting trainings I ask providers to begin by describing their immediate reactions to the term BPD. Consistently, responses include such descriptions as "difficult," "gamey," "manipulative," "demanding," "self-injurious," "suicidal," "untreatable," "dramatic," "emotional," and "unpredictable." One survey of mental health providers indicated that 84% of these providers reported that dealing with Borderlines was more difficult than any other patient group (Cleary, Siegfried, & Walter, 2002). Providers not only express attitudes that they will be unable to be helpful to such individuals, but also fears that they will be sued or harassed by these clients.

Such descriptions, even if true (and I would argue that most are not true), provide little hope or guidance as to what to do in dealing with these individuals. Thus, providers face these clients not only lacking effective strategies, but also impaired by negative attitudes that do nothing to create trust or positive regard between the client and provider. Such attitudes only lead to behaviors which further perpetuate the Borderline's feelings of alienation and lack of trust. Further, they leave the provider feeling inadequate, frustrated and helpless. The result is a culture which reinforces a view of working with these clients as an unending and miserable struggle.

Many providers choose to deal with these struggles by avoiding working with Borderlines altogether. One participant indicated *"I was advised by the malpractice folks to refer all borderlines to my worst enemies."* While providers in private practice may have the luxury of choosing not to work with Borderlines, most human services providers, especially those in community mental health, emergency services or inpatient settings, cannot avoid contact with Borderlines. Further, clients with BPD can look deceptively well during first contacts and thus, it is often not apparent to the provider that he or she is dealing with a Borderline until problems develop.

While professionals certainly should know their own limits and set boundaries about what clients they feel competent and capable of treating, it is ultimately unhelpful to "give up" or avoid working with these individuals. Imagine if all brain surgeons gave up conducting surgery because it was difficult, has a high mortality rate, and high risk of law suit! Instead some individuals choose this profession and learn to manage the stress and risk of such difficult work. Likewise, there is a need for brave and innovative professionals who are willing to take on the challenges and risks inherent in treating these difficult clients. These individuals need to be equipped with both effective strategies and new attitudes toward these clients in order to be more successful and also to make the work more pleasurable and less stressful.

Research supports the need and desire of mental health providers for assistance in becoming more effective with these individuals. In one study, mental health staff completed a survey with regard to their knowledge and attitudes toward clients with BPD (Cleary, Siegfried, & Walter, 2002). 85% of the providers reported having contact with Borderline clients once a month or more frequently. 32% reported daily contact with Borderlines. 80% of providers reported feeling that dealing with clients who have BPD is "moderately" to "very" difficult. 84% of these providers felt that dealing with Borderlines was more difficult than any other patient group. 95% indicated a willingness to gain further education and training in the management of these clients.

Borderline Personality Disorder: Struggling, Understanding, Succeeding is intended to provide such training in language easily understandable to clinicians of all backgrounds. The title is intended to describe not only the process the individual with BPD goes through in recovering, but also the process providers must go through to live with and treat BPD as well. The struggling client with BPD must learn to understand her behavior in order to change it. Likewise, the struggling clinician must learn to understand the Borderline client before they will be able to provide successful interventions.

THE CLIENT'S STRUGGLE

"Everyone expects me to have goals for the future.
I'm just struggling to survive each day."

—Client with BPD

Such is the struggle of persons with Borderline Personality Disorder (BPD). Plagued by chronic urges to harm themselves, overwhelming emotions, impulsivity, and/or conflictual relationships, every day, and sometimes, every moment, is a struggle to get through. The tasks of every day life which most people seem to handle with minimal discomfort leave the Borderline client feeling confused, overwhelmed, and inadequate.

Each Borderline's struggle and experience is unique, yet there tend to be common themes to the Borderline experience. Life has almost always been hard for these individuals. Their backgrounds are often filled with chaos, instability, trauma, and/or abuse. Even those with a relatively stable family of origin have erratic relationships with their loved ones. Impulsive behaviors such as alcohol and drug use, spending, and emotional outbursts create further chaos in their lives. Many are chronically angry and depressed and vacillate between blowing up at others and turning in on themselves.

Compounding these difficulties are the natural, but unhelpful reactions and attitudes of those around them. Loved ones, providers, and the community tend to view these individuals' erratic behavior as "manipulative," "attention seeking," and "selfish" implying that they want to live this way and could easily change things if they would just "try harder." The prevailing attitude seems to be that these individuals "get off" on making life miserable for everyone. Such attitudes only leave the client feeling more confused, inadequate, isolated and ashamed. Further, even if such attitudes are true, they provide little information as to how to help these individuals.

THE COMMUNITY'S STRUGGLE

Such reactions by those who come into contact with Borderlines are not without justification. Persons with BPD create difficulties for those who try to live with them and help them. These individuals are perpetually in crisis yet do things that exacerbate their crisis. When others try to assist they either reject help or become completely dependent. They tend to idealize or devalue others resulting in a view of others as "all good" or "all bad." This results in a "no win" situations for those who care for individuals with BPD. As a result many who start out eager to help become frustrated, angry and exhausted.

Further, these clients tend to seek assistance from multiple sources leading to an enormous amount of energy and resources being devoted to their care. Families, churches, social service departments, police departments, medical providers and others all struggle in their contacts with Borderlines. They tend to be high utilizers of mental health and medical services, and are often involved in the legal or social service systems because of their impulsive and sometimes aggressive behavior. Their difficulties in interpersonal relationships can create havoc in religious communities.

Thus, it is critical that not only mental health therapists but also other human service professionals be educated regarding the dynamics of BPD and effective ways of understanding and intervening with these individuals.

2

Struggling to Define Borderline Personality Disorder

Borderline Personality Disorder is a controversial, complex topic. Just defining it is like trying to catch a fish with your bare hands, blindfolded and in the rain.

Stop Walking on Eggshells: Taking Back Your Life When Someone You Care About Has Borderline Personality Disorder
—Randi Kreger

Not only is it difficult to live with BPD, it is difficult to define and explain the disorder as well. Adding to this difficulty, the term "Borderline" itself provides no useful information as to the characteristics of this disorder. Why is it called "Borderline" and what does that mean?

HISTORICAL FOUNDATIONS OF BPD

The term "Borderline" first appeared in the psychoanalytic literature in the early 1900s. However, literary examples of individuals who would likely meet criteria for the diagnosis date back to at least the 16th century (Lawson, 2002). Further, BPD has been reported to be present in many cultures around the world (APA, 2001).

Originally, analysts used this term for clients who appeared appropriate for psychoanalysis but later proved to have difficulty with the process. Early psychoanalytic theoretical descriptions of the "Borderline" fell into two categories. One group saw these clients as having a mild form of schizophrenia or as "borderline" schizophrenics. The other group saw them as a distinct group who were neither neurotic nor psychotic but operated psychologically on a level between psychosis and neurosis. Thus, they described these clients as being in the "border" between psychosis and neurosis.

Early writings describing these clients were common as they did not seem to fit the usual psychodynamic theories and did not respond to treatment as expected. In 1967, Otto Kernberg wrote a seminal paper entitled "Borderline Personality Organization" which integrated these earlier writings and provided a comprehensive framework for understanding the disorder. This framework was based on sophisticated psychoanalytic theory that is difficult to understand for those who are not analytically trained. Nonetheless, this work integrated the earlier discussions and provides an interesting historical reference for the understanding of the disorder.

In spite of its prevalence, BPD did not gain official diagnostic status until 1980 when, like the other personality disorders, it was officially adopted as a diagnostic entity in the DSM-III nomenclature. At that time there was little debate regarding the disorder's presence or features but great debate as to what it should be called. The following excerpt from Theodore Millon's June 1978 memo to the DSM-III committee summarizes the concerns with this label (Millon, 1981).

> I would like to register my strong agreement with the point raised . . . to the effect that the label, borderline is perhaps the most poorly chosen of all the terms selected for the DSM-III. I know a small segment of the profession feels that this is the most apt descriptive term for this population, but frankly, I find the word, borderline, to mean, at best, a level of severity and not a descriptive type . . . Unless the word is used to signify a class the borders on something, then it has no clinical or descriptive meaning at all . . .
>
> I would like the Personality Committee to reassess the term borderline . . .other alternative labels that might be considered are the following: ambivalent personality disorder, erratic personality disorder, impulsive personality disorder, quixotic personality disorder, etc. Any one of these would be far preferable than the meaningless borderline label.

As Millon indicates, unless one is using the term to describe a level of functioning in relationship to some other level of functioning, the term "borderline" itself is meaningless. However, because early use of the term had become associated with a class of clients in the professional community, the term stuck. It remains to be seen whether or not the term will be eventually changed to something more descriptive and consistent with current theoretical understandings.

Unfortunately, imprecision in nomenclature only adds to the struggle of these clients because their diagnostic label adds nothing to the understanding of their concerns. Thus, using this term with clients and their loved ones is seldom useful unless it is accompanied by a concrete description of the kinds of struggles such clients experience.

This became increasingly apparent to me as I began traveling to speak on BPD. Friends without mental health training often ask me what I speak about. If I respond "Depression" or "Antisocial Personality Disorder," the response is often "That's interesting, you know I knew someone who . . ." If I respond "Borderline Personality Disorder," I am met with looks of confusion and the topic is abruptly changed.

Friends with mental health training however, respond with knowing looks and groans or sighs. Ones' first experience with a Borderline's angry outburst or self injury is something few clinicians forget. But while mental health providers tend to have an intuitive understanding of the disorder, they often cannot articulate a concrete and accurate description of its characteristics. Unfortunately this can lead to misdiagnosis and inaccurate judgments about clients. So how do we concretely define BPD?

DSM-IV DIAGNOSTIC CRITERIA

To understand BPD more clearly, one must first turn to the diagnostic criteria as described in the Diagnostic and Statistical Manual of Mental Disorders, Fourth Edition (DSM-IV). The reader is referred to the DSM-IV for the specific criteria which will be summarized here.

ONSET & PERVASIVENESS

One of the most important features of BPD is the pervasiveness of the symptoms in the client's life. Many individuals may at one time or another experience one or more of the nine diagnostic criteria but for those with BPD these symptoms are chronic and pervasive. Often misdiagnosis may occur when an individual, at some crisis point in their life, exhibits several of the symptoms but historical information reveals that this is an isolated episode rather than part of a "pervasive pattern." Thus, it is critical to obtain adequate historical information in order to make an accurate diagnosis.

For this reason, the diagnostic criteria includes a statement regarding the onset and prevalence of such symptoms.

> A *pervasive* pattern of instability of interpersonal relationships, self-image, and affects, and marked impulsivity *beginning by early adulthood and present in a variety of contexts*. (emphasis added)

Note that the instability of relationships, self-image, and affects must be a "pervasive pattern." In other words this isn't a one time conflictual romantic relationship or a temporary disruption in self-concept or mood. These clients have *chronic* or episodic difficulties in *many* relationships. Unlike brief disruptions in self-image brought about by life changes or traumatic events, these clients continuously have difficulty defining who they are and/or have a pervasive negative self-concept. They have difficulty regulating their emotions not only under stress but in the face of seemingly minor events as well. These difficulties do not just occur in isolated situations such as school or home but "in a variety of contexts."

Also important is the onset of the symptoms. By definition, one does not suddenly develop BPD at age 40! This pervasive pattern must be present "by early adulthood" which means somewhere in the late teens or early 20s. Thus, such symptoms are present by the time the individual has developed a characteristic way of being in the world or "personality." Further, by definition, these symptoms are not just part of a "stage" in the client's development but are a well established pattern of interacting with the world.

Sometimes these criteria are erroneously interpreted to mean that adolescents can not be diagnosed as having a personality disorder. While caution should be used in labeling a teenager as borderline because of the stigma attached to the label, there are cases where such a label may be appropriate. However, here again, the pervasiveness of the pattern is the key consideration. In addition one must consider whether or not the symptoms are part of a developmental process or if they have become an established manner of interacting with the world.

For example, many would argue that most girls in Jr. High experience affective instability, impulsivity, identity disturbance, and unstable relationships! With the onset of puberty comes moodiness and questions of "Who am I?" Adolescents may change clothes, styles, interests, and friends at the drop of the hat. A friend or boyfriend may be "wonderful" one day and "terrible" the next. However, these explorations of self usually resolve into a general sense of themselves, their likes and dislikes, and their companions.

For the Borderline individual such inconsistencies are not just temporary explorations but chronic difficulties. If such difficulties persist without resolution, and are accompanied by the other symptoms, then a diagnosis of BPD may be appropriate for the adolescent. Thus, I tend to use the diagnosis only in later adolescents and only when there is a preponderance of evidence in the absence of alternative diagnosis.

SYMPTOMS

The individual diagnostic criteria are generally self-explanatory, however, it can be beneficial to understand ways in which such symptoms typically manifest themselves in BPD. It should be noted that each set of symptoms may be present with other disorders and it is only when several (5 of 9 criteria) are met in a pervasive pattern that the diagnosis is warranted.

Criterion 1 and 2 are related to relationship issues and include "frantic efforts to avoid real or imagined abandonment" and "a pattern of unstable and intense interpersonal relationships characterized by alternating between extremes of idealization and devaluation." Linehan (1993) refers to these two symptoms as "interpersonal dysregulation."

Clients with BPD have difficulty maintaining long term relationships. They are very sensitive to perceived rejection and will attempt to "be good" to avoid the loss of the relationship. Families, churches, social service departments, police departments, medical providers and others struggle in their contacts with Borderlines.

Frequently, these clients will excessively ask a provider or loved one "Are you mad?" They fear that if they have angered an important person he or she will leave them emotionally or physically. A therapeutic response in this situation would be to honestly describe one's feelings but include reassurance that being angry doesn't mean you don't care or will leave. The Borderline needs reassurance that in spite of your emotional state you will continue the relationship with them.

A common example of Criterion 2 is the Borderline who comes into the new therapist's office and complains continuously about a prior provider or another individual. This is usually followed by generous praise and statements about how much more understanding and trustworthy you are. At that point the other individual is "all bad" and you are "all good." While this feeds our countertransference and desire to be appreciated, rest assured that eventually you will do something that will knock you off your pedestal. A therapeutic response to this situation is to try to make observations about both the good and bad in others and in ourselves. I often thank the client with BPD for their compliments and then proceed to warn them of my human frailties. I advise them that at some point I will disappoint and/or anger them.

Criteria 3 and 7 have to do with issues of identity and fulfillment. Linehan (1993) refers to these criteria as "dysregulation of the self." However, the client with BPD does not walk into your office and announce "I have a markedly unstable self-image!" Instead there will be comments like, "I don't know who I am." "When I'm in a room I just watch everyone else and try to figure out how to act." Further, they will have difficulties completing activities such as goal setting, self collages, lists of things they like, lists of traits about themselves, or autobiographies as these activities require a sense of themselves and their identity. Feelings of emptiness are often described by these clients in the following manner. "I feel like there's a black hole inside of me that will never be filled." "I'm just numb." "I know people love me but I just can't feel it."

Criteria 4 and 5 have to do with impulsive behaviors that are in some way self destructive including self injurious behavior. Linehan (1993) refers to these symptoms as "behavioral dysregulation." This can include things such as chemical use, driving too fast, or promiscuity, but can also include self destructive behavior such as quitting jobs or school impulsively or abruptly discontinuing medication or therapy. Two such types of behavior must be present to meet criteria 4.

Criterion 5 is specific to suicidal or intentionally self-injurious behavior. It is important to note that BPD is the only psychiatric disorder in which self injury is part of the diagnostic criteria. Not all Borderlines self injure but a high percentage (about 80%) engage in this behavior at some point. Likewise, not everyone who self injures is Borderline. Nonetheless, self-injurious behavior is often thought of as the hallmark of BPD. Interventions for self-injurious behavior will be discussed in detail in Chapter 5.

Criteria 6 and 8 have to do with mood related symptoms. Linehan (1993) calls these symptoms "emotional dysregulation" and states that this problem underlies all the other symptoms which occur in BPD. Borderlines tend to be described as "moody" individuals who "can be fine one minute and fly into a rage the next." Many Borderlines have particular difficulty with the expression of anger. Either they are chronically angry and irritable and/or they have episodic angry outbursts. Often significant others describe them as being "like Dr. Jekyll and Mr. Hyde." It is important to note that such mood symptoms tend to be of relatively short duration and are often in reaction to interpersonal issues.

Linehan (1993) refers to criteria 9 as "cognitive dysregulation" which includes the transient cognitive symptoms of dissociation and paranoia. These symptoms tend to be present more in times of acute stressors rather than the chronic presence in the psychotic disorders. Frequently the dissociation with take the form of "checking out" during a session as indicated by the client staring at the floor or into space with a blank look. Clients will also describe dissociating either prior to or during episodes of self injury. "I felt like I was disappearing and it (cutting) brought me back." Or "I don't feel anything when I'm doing it (burning). It just makes me numb."

The paranoia identified here can take the form of bizarre delusions (e.g. "The FBI is monitoring me through my t.v.") however, these are much less common in persons with BPD. More common is a heightened sensitivity to and over personalization of interpersonal stimuli (e.g. "I saw them talking in the corner and I know they're talking about what a loser I am."). Borderlines will also sometimes report auditory hallucinations which most often take the form of self critical statements or command hallucinations telling the client to harm themselves.

Again, while individuals *without* BPD may at times exhibit any or all of these traits, the individual with BPD exhibits a *chronic and pervasive pattern* of 5 or more of these traits and this pattern was present *by early adulthood*. Understanding these traits can be helpful to providers who need to communicate information to the physician or psychologist making the diagnosis. Further, because many of these traits can be present or similar in other disorders it is important to understand the full diagnostic picture to avoid misdiagnosis. Finally, it can be helpful for the individual dealing with the Borderline to understand that these traits are part of their illness, not conscious attempts to manipulate or cause problems.

ASSESSMENT

Obviously, the initial assessment of these individuals must first focus on suicide risk and issues of safety to determine an appropriate level of care. These issues will be further addressed in Chapter 5. After this risk assessment, a standard diagnostic interview including a thorough psychosocial history is warranted. Because the disorder is defined by a pervasive pattern of interacting with the world, a thorough history is necessary to establish the presence of the diagnostic criteria over time and beginning by early adulthood. For this reason, assessment should not only consist of one or more clinical interviews with the client, but obtaining records of prior treatments and consulting with collateral sources of information (family, friends, etc.) as well.

There are some diagnostic tools which may be useful in confirming the diagnosis but frankly these are seldom necessary if a good diagnostic interview has been completed and records obtained. The exception to this may be for research purposes when the diagnosis must be standardized and corroborated or in settings where a self administered assessment tool may expedite the interview in an attempt to deal with time limitations. Table 1 summarizes some of the more common assessment tools specific to BPD as well as findings on some of the most commonly used psychometric assessment tools.

Table 1: Summary of Assessment Tools for Diagnosing BPD

Assessment Tool	**Source**	**Type**	**Comments**
Borderline Personality Disorder Severity Index	Leichsenring, (1999).	53 item, True/False Self Report	Based on Kernberg's Psychodynamic formulation of BPD and compatible with DSM-IV diagnostic criteria. Provides a cut-off score for diagnosis. Good reliability, sensitivity, and specificity.

Table 1: Summary of Assessment Tools for Diagnosing BPD (Continued)

Assessment Tool	Source	Type	Comments
Borderline Personality Inventory	Arntz, van de Hoorn, Corneli, Verheul, van den Bosch, Wies, de Bie (2003)	Semistructured interview.	Good reliability and internal consistency. Good discriminant validity. Good sensitivity to improvement making it appropriate for outcome research.
Diagnostic Interview of Borderline Personality Disorder (DIB-R)	Zanarini, Gunderson, Frankenburg & Chancey, (1989)	1-hour semi-structured interview based on DSM-II-R Criteria	Strong Reliability, Sensitivity & Specificity for the Diagnosis.
Personality Assessment Inventory (PAI)	Morey, (1991)	344 item inventory	Good reliability and validity data. 22 scales including four borderline feature subscales: Affective Instability, Identity Problems, Negative Relationships, and Self-Harm.
Millon Clinical Multi-Axial Inventory III (MCMI)	NCS	Self-report questionnaire comprised of True/False Statements	Based on Millon's taxonomy for personality disorders. Inadequate convergent or discriminate validity.
Minnesota Multiphasic Psychological Inventory (MMPI-2)	NCS	567 True/False Statements	No clear pattern of results that distinguishes BPD from other disorders. High F scores and overall elevations are common.

Table 1: Summary of Assessment Tools for Diagnosing BPD (Continued)

Assessment Tool	Source	Type	Comments
Rorschach (Exner Scoring Method)	Gartner, Hurt, & Gartner (1989)	Projective test based on responses to 10 inkblots.	No specific profile. However, clients with BPD tend to display the following: Lower D scores, High Egocentricity Index, Minimal thought disorder without evidence of severe thought disorder, High affective ratios, Poor form quality, Poor emotion regulation as evidenced by high Sum of Shading & Color Responses.
Structured Clinical Interview for the DSM-III-R Personality Disorders (SCID-II)	Spitzer, Williams, & Gibbon, (1987)	Structured Interview based on DSM-III-R Criteria for Axis I & Axis II Disorders.	Strong Validity & Interrater reliability.

PREVALENCE OF BPD

The prevalence of BPD in the general population is estimated at anywhere from .2 to 15 percent (Swartz, et al., 1990). Approximately 10 percent of psychiatric outpatients have a BPD while 15 to 20% of psychiatric inpatients have BPD (Swartz, et. al., 1990; Dean, 1991). While such numbers may not seem terrifically impressive, they become very concerning when one considers the utilization pattern and subsequent cost of treatment for these individuals. It is estimated that 75 to 80% of inpatient dollars are spent on 30 to 35% of the patients. In other words, a small number of individuals use the greater portion of treatment resources. Studies of utilization of mental health services indicate that 9 to 40% of high utilizers are diagnosed with BPD (Dean, 1991). Thus, while this may not be one of the most common disorders, persons with BPD utilize a significant portion of treatment resources. This adds to the frustration and hopelessness of providers and makes improvement of treatment methods even more critical.

BPD is 2 to 4 times more common in women and it is for this reason that the feminine pronoun is used throughout this book to refer to clients with BPD. In part this may be due to a gender bias in diagnosis in which women are more likely to be diagnosed as Borderline and put in the mental health system while men may be more likely to be diagnosed as having Antisocial or Narcissistic personality disorder and put in the corrections system. However, the differing rates of occurrence may also result from real gender difference and cultural factors.

Several possible explanations for such differences exist. As will be discussed in Chapter 3, history of abuse seems to be one factor placing an individual at risk for developing BPD. Since women are statistically more likely to be abused this may place them at greater risk for development of the disorder. In addition, at least one theory of etiology proposes that a significant risk factor is difficulty in emotion regulation. Because women tend to be both biologically and culturally more oriented to relational and emotional stimuli, they may be more vulnerable to problems in this area. Further, the hormonal factors associated with child bearing may contribute to emotion regulation difficulties. To put it bluntly, anyone who has experienced or lived with someone with PMS knows that hormones strongly affect mood and mood regulation! Any combination of these factors may make women more vulnerable to the development of this disorder.

At least one study found that the occurrence of BPD was greater in "non-whites" than whites (Swartz, et al., 1990). However, due to methodological concerns, this finding should be confirmed in further research. Specifically, the tool used to assess for the presence of BPD tended to look only at the presence of symptoms and not at the prevalence and pervasiveness criteria.

Nonetheless, these findings raise a number of cultural concerns which should be considered. First, there may be racism in the application of the diagnosis with some tendency to be more likely to attribute this label to people of color. Second, people of color may be prone to cultural factors such as increased rates of poverty, malnutrition, and trauma which may increase the etiological risk factors for development of the disorder. Finally, cultural bias in assessment of behavior may be a factor. Specifically, what is considered "affective instability" and/or "inappropriate anger" may differ significantly depending on the cultural context of the individual. Thus, it is critical in making the diagnosis to consider whether or not the individual's behavior in consistent with their cultural context. Again, further research with regard to cultural factors in this disorder is needed.

The highest rates for presence of the disorder are at ages 19 to 34 (Swartz, et.al. 1990). This makes sense as given the pervasiveness criteria one would expect few confirmed cases prior to early adulthood. Further, the rate of psychiatric disorders in general is highest in this age groups with many disorders showing substantial improvement in middle adulthood. Likewise, Borderline symptoms, especially the impulsive behavior, do improve over time. Recovery rates are further discussed in Chapter 6.

PROGNOSTIC INDICATORS

Several prognostic indicators have been explored in long-term follow-up studies of BPD (Dean, 2001; Paris, Brown & Nowlis, 1987; Plakun, 1991; Ryle & Golynkina, 2000).

Obviously, those with the most severe symptoms have a poorer prognosis. Longer hospitalizations is also associated with poorer outcomes but this is correlational research not causal research so it is impossible to determine to what extent those with shorter hospitalizations were less severely impaired to begin with. However, as will be discussed in Chapter 5 shorter hospitalizations tend to be preferred for Borderlines as long hospitalizations tend to lead to regression, dependence on the system, and difficulty transferring skills to an outpatient setting.

Other factors include the presence of dysphoria, substance abuse, unemployment, and strong antisocial traits. All of which tend to be poor prognostic signs as well. History of family mental illness and a younger age when first seen for treatment may also predict a poorer outcome.

COMORBIDITY AND DIFFERENTIAL DIAGNOSIS

Part of the difficulty in diagnosing BPD is that the presence of other disorders is so common. Further complicating the picture is the fact that patients with other disorders may possess Borderline traits but not meet full diagnostic criteria and vice versa. 60% of Borderlines meet full criteria for other disorders with the most common comorbid disorders being Anxiety Disorders and Major Depression. (Grilo, et al., 2003; Swartz, et al., 1990; Zanarini, et al. 1998).

One study found a lifetime prevalence of other disorders at 100%. However, based on the research design it is impossible to tell if clients actually met criteria for other disorders or were previously misdiagnosed. In fact patients with BPD will often be given a number of other diagnosis before the Borderline diagnosis is settled upon. Thus, when one sees a client with multiple prior diagnosis this may indicate the dramatic fluctuations in presentation that typifies BPD and should raise a red flag for the clinician to evaluate for the presence of BPD.

Such diagnostic clarification is important yet difficult. Rather than become stuck in a diagnostic quagmire, the clinician should evaluate whether or not a change in diagnosis will significantly effect the treatment plan. For example, a client with Bipolar Disorder who is moody and impulsive would likely be treated with a mood stabilizer, taught mood regulation skills, and given interpersonal and problem solving skills to clean up the problems created while in a mood state. Likewise, a client who is Borderline who has significant mood instability would likely be treated with a mood stabilizer, taught mood regulation skills, and given interpersonal and problem solving skills. If clarifying the diagnosis does not substantially alter the treatment course, the clinician should make their "best guess" based on the information available and err on the conservative side by recognizing the stigma attached to the Borderline label. In making such an evaluation, it is helpful to be familiar with comorbidity rates and key factors that may aid in differentiating each diagnosis.

Anxiety and Depressive Disorders commonly co-occur with BPD (Grilo, et al., 2003; Swartz, et al., 1990; Zanarini, et al. 1998). Because Borderlines tend to exhibit a high overall anxiety level, Generalized Anxiety Disorder is particularly common. Dysthymia and Depression also occur at a high rate. These disorders are not particularly difficult to differentiate because there is not a great deal of diagnostic criteria overlap and one can easily review the diagnostic criteria for each disorder.

Given the frequent history of trauma in clients with BPD, Comorbid Post Traumatic Stress Disorder (PTSD) is common but not universal. PTSD can be difficult to differentiate as both clients with PTSD and Borderlines tend to have traumatic histories and to dissociate. However, trauma related symptoms such as flashbacks, nightmares, and exaggerated startle response occur in PTSD but are not part of the clinical picture for BPD. If a Borderline client also has these symptoms then a PTSD diagnosis is also appropriate.

In addition, clients with PTSD tend to dissociate in response to a specific trauma related stimuli whereas clients with BPD tend to dissociate indiscriminately in response to stress. For example, a client with PTSD due to industrial injury tends to dissociate whenever he hears helicopters (trauma related stimuli) as they remind him of being air lifted to a trauma hospital. A client with BPD dissociates in session when discussing any topic with heavy emotional content or when demands are placed on her causing stress.

Clients with BPD also tend to dissociate just prior to, or during self injury. Those who report feeling no pain during self injury are likely to have higher rates of dissociation and should also be evaluated for a diagnosis of a Dissociative Disorder (Kemperman, Russ, & Shearin, 1997; Sar, et. al., 2003)

Bipolar Disorder, more commonly known as Manic-Depressive illness, can be particularly difficult to differentiate from BPD as both involve rapid mood swings, impulsive behavior, and interpersonal problems. However, in Bipolar Disorder the mood symptoms tend to be longer in duration (2 weeks or more) where as in BPD the swings are shorter in duration ("lasting a few hours and only rarely more than a few days"). The exception to this of course is the "rapid cycling" form of Bipolar Disorder which is especially difficult to differentiate from BPD.

However, in Bipolar Disorder the mood symptoms tend to occur at random and *result in* interpersonal problems (e.g. Client wakes up euphoric one morning and goes out drinking and has a one night stand.). In contrast, in BPD the mood swings tend to be more in response to environmental situations and are a *result of* interpersonal problems (e.g. Client meets someone at a bar and strikes up a relationship which makes her euphorically happy until after a night of sex the partner dumps her at which point she becomes depressed and suicidal).

Finally, in making the differential diagnosis one should assess the client's family history for presence of Bipolar Disorder. Bipolar Disorder has very strong genetic linkage. If there is family history of Bipolar disorder it is highly likely that the client also has Bipolar Disorder and mood stabilizing agents are strongly indicated. Some clinicians have suggested that clients with "true" Bipolar disorder respond more rapidly and dramatically to mood stabilizers than those with "true" BPD. While this is generally true, in my experience clients with BPD can also respond fairly dramatically

A number of clients with BPD also meet diagnostic criteria for eating disorders however, BPD is no more common in clients with eating disorders than any other Axis I or Axis II diagnosis (Grilo, et. al., 2003). My clinical experience suggests that it may more commonly occur with bulimia but this impression may be a result of the higher incidence of bulimia than anorexia. Certainly, I have seen both in my practice and I am unaware of any research findings in this area.

The difficulty in differentiating BPD from eating disorders primarily results from the fact that some Borderlines engage in purging or restricting behaviors as one of the potentially self damaging impulsive behaviors. To clarify the diagnosis the clinician should ask questions to evaluate what function the behavior serves and to determine if weight concerns and disturbance in body image are present. Borderlines tend to describe the behavior as an attempt to regulate mood ("I just feel better after I do it." Or "I just get so upset I have to.") whereas those with an eating disorder describe the problematic behaviors as an attempt to control weight ("I knew I ate too much and I had to get rid of the calories." Or "I ate too much and I had to get rid of it."). In addition, clients with BPD deny concerns with weight whereas those with eating disorders describe themselves as "fat" and are often obsessed with their weight and/or food.

It is generally not too difficult to determine if a client with BPD also has an Addictive Disorder. If they meet dependence criteria such as increased tolerance, withdrawal symptoms, etc. then clearly they have comorbid substance dependence. Many Borderlines periodically use chemicals excessively, usually as a means of regulating their mood and/or as one of the impulsive self destructive behaviors. Depending on the frequency and degree of such use they may also qualify for a Chemical Abuse diagnosis.

Misdiagnosis is most likely to occur when an individual who is actively using chemicals displays many of the behaviors consistent with BPD. Intoxication and/or attempts to obtain chemicals may often lead to impulsive behavior, mood swings, and interpersonal conflicts. Withdrawal symptoms may include irritability, mood swings, and angry outbursts. The key question is whether or not such behaviors only occur only during use and/or withdrawal or if they are a more pervasive part of the individual's personality regardless of use. This can be especially difficult to determine in the chemically dependent young adult as they may have minimal periods of sobriety and it may be hard to obtain reports of their functioning during these times. In these cases the BPD diagnosis is best delayed until their behavior can be observed during a substantial period of sobriety.

Other Personality Disorders can also co-exist with BPD and are generally not difficult to distinguish with consideration of a few factors. Clients with BPD will at times engage in antisocial behaviors however they tend to view these behaviors as necessary to their survival and will later recognize them as wrong, feel extremely guilty, and show remorse. For example the Borderline client may steal medication in order to overdose when she doesn't have the cash to pay for it or is concerned about getting caught with it. She recognizes stealing as wrong and often will later make attempts to make amends. Clients with Antisocial Personality engage in such behaviors because they feel entitled to do so, show little remorse, and little recognition of how their behavior effects others. Borderlines with strong antisocial traits are often especially difficult to treat because guilt and remorse can often be a powerful motivator for changing behavior.

Borderlines are often described as narcissistic or "self-centered" and indeed at times they act with little consideration of the impact of their behavior on others. However, this tends to be in times of acute distress and as a function of their being too overwhelmed to think about others. Again, they will later show guilt and remorse.

In contrast, those with Narcissistic Personality Disorder seldom, if ever, "get" the negative impact of their behavior and feel completely entitled to act the way they do. They tend to always blame others whereas the Borderline client will alternate between blaming others and blaming themselves. Narcissists do not admit to needing others and do not fear abandonment as others are not that important to them. In contrast, Borderlines are often open regarding their neediness and fear abandonment by others.

Clients with Dependent Personality Disorder will also express fears of abandonment due to their need for others to make decisions for them. However, they typically are much more emotionally reserved, passive, and not especially impulsive. In contrast, Borderlines vacillate between being needy and helpless and needing to be totally in control.

Because clients with BPD are at times "dramatic" in their presentation this can be confused with Histrionic Personality Disorder. However, clients with Histrionic Personality Disorder are dramatic all the time. They tend to function very well in life, gravitate toward professions that reward their flamboyance, and seldom seek treatment unless an interpersonal conflict arises. In contrast, Borderlines will alternate between dramatic outbursts and affective restriction, tend to function poorly overall, and often come to the attention of treatment providers.

Schizotypal Personality Disorder is seldom confused with BPD but confusion does occasionally occur. During an acute crisis, borderlines can exhibit restriction of affect and psychotic thinking. However this is a temporary state which may be replaced at other times with dramatic displays of emotions. The Schizotypal client, on the other hand, consistently displays restricted affect and his or her psychotic thoughts are chronic and persistent in nature.

Unfortunately, persons with Developmental Disabilities, more commonly known as Mental Retardation, are sometimes misdiagnosed with BPD. While on very rare occasions there may be mildly developmentally disabled individual who also clearly meets the diagnostic criteria for BPD, in most cases such a diagnosis is inappropriate. Most often this misdiagnosis occurs when the individual engages in self injurious behavior or makes repeated suicidal innuendos (i.e. "I wish I was dead!"). Such behaviors are then erroneously interpreted to mean that the client has BPD.

In many cases, the same neurological condition that caused the client's developmental disability causes high rates of self injury. Self injurious behavior and statements such as "I wish I was dead!" are very primitive responses to stressors. In most cases they are primitive ways of expressing frustration or other negative affect for individuals who lack the verbal capacity to express these feelings. It must be emphasized that self injurious behavior is only one of the needed criteria for BPD and does not in and of itself substantiate the diagnosis.

Clients with developmental disabilities may also exhibit impulsive behavior, moodiness, or angry outbursts. Again however, these must be considered within the context of their cognitive abilities and in light of the biological conditions causing their delays. If the behavior is consistent with the client's cognitive abilities and/or neurological condition, a diagnosis of BPD is unwarranted.

To put it bluntly, one must have enough IQ points to have a personality for it to be disordered! I do not mean this to be disrespectful of those with developmental delays and certainly, those of us who have known these individuals know they definitely have personality! However, one must consider if their behavior is consistent with their cognitive and social functioning level or if the individual is "capable" of better functioning. Because in most cases such behaviors are a result of their differing abilities the diagnosis of BPD should be made only in the presence of overwhelming evidence and lack of alternative explanations. However, it should be noted in terms of treatment that some of the same skills need to be learned by both the individual who exhibits these behaviors due to developmental disability and those who exhibit these skills due to BPD. Thus, there is overlap in the treatment approaches especially in regard to specific skills training.

CASE EXAMPLES

To illustrate and apply the information presented in this chapter, consider the following case examples:

> Case Scenario #1: 21-year-old female presents for outpatient therapy at community mental health center. She is referred by the county and is currently under mental health commitment. She was hospitalized last week due to a suicide attempt by overdose.
>
> This was precipitated by a fight with her boyfriend in which he stated that he wanted to end the relationship. Apparently she came home drunk and accused him of being involved with someone else. Her boyfriend states they have been on again and off again for over a year. He describes her as moody & irritable. "She drinks too much. Even when she's not drinking she has terrible mood swings. She can be fine one minute and fly into a rage the next."
>
> Client reports a long history of mental health treatment with at least five hospitalizations due to suicide attempts. There is a history of childhood sexual abuse. There is also indication that she has a history of cutting on herself as the admitting physician noted scarring on her forearms.
>
> Client states upon admission, "I don't know why I'm here. I shouldn't have gotten so mad but he doesn't really care about me. No one does. I may as well be dead."

Based on the information provided, this client would likely meet criteria for BPD. Her history of multiple hospitalizations suggest that this is an ongoing pattern although one would want to obtain more information on the pervasiveness of many of the symptoms. Since she is only age 21 these concerns are clearly present by early adulthood. She clearly meets criteria 5 with a history of at least five suicide attempts and apparent cutting on her forearms.

Several other symptoms are clearly suggested and could easily be confirmed in terms of their prevalence. Criteria 1 (abandonment) is suggested as the current difficulties were precipitated by the boyfriend's attempt to end the relationship although this should be confirmed by other examples and in other relationships. Criteria 2 (unstable relationships) is also suggested as at least this relationship is described as unstable. This should be confirmed by evaluating the quality of other relationships. Criteria 3 (identity disturbance) or Criteria 7 (emptiness) may be suggested by her statement "I don't know why I'm here . . . He doesn't care about me. No one does." However, one would want further confirmation of this as well as asking her more about what she means by these statements. Criteria 6 (affective instability) and Criteria 8 (inappropriate anger) are reported by her boyfriend although again, confirmation in other situations and by other reporters is warranted. Finally, her drinking is one example of Criteria 4 (impulsive self-damaging behavior) and one would look for other examples to confirm this criteria.

Other diagnoses would need to be ruled out as well. In particular, an assessment of her chemical use is warranted. If the above behaviors are only present during periods of use they may be chemically induced rather than part of her personality structure and an Addictive disorder diagnosis is more appropriate. If these traits are present when she is not using, she may still qualify for a comorbid addictive diagnosis in addition to BPD. PTSD and Bipolar disorder should also be ruled out in this case.

> Case Scenario # 2: Client is a 27-year-old married female whose husband has referred her to an outpatient mental health clinic due to concerns that she is vomiting after supper. They reported she has had problems with this in the past but had not done this for at least a year. Over the past two months she is vomiting about twice a week.
>
> The couple has been married for five years. He describes her as a "perfectionist" and is concerned "she puts too much pressure on herself." She reports she is "stressed out" about work and home responsibilities. "I just get so frustrated and angry. I know I shouldn't do it but I feel better afterward."
>
> She denies restricting food, excessive exercise, or concerns regarding her body image. She is thin, her hair appears thin, and she acknowledges being "cold a lot." Regarding the vomiting she

states, "I'm not doing it to lose weight. I just get so upset I feel like I have to." She reports that in the past when upset she has hit or scratched herself. She denies previous mental health treatment. She denies history of abuse. She does report sleep disturbance and anhedonia. She does report one sibling has been treated for depression and both her siblings have a history of cutting and/or hitting themselves when upset.

This case is more difficult to discern. On the one had she is described as moody and irritable. She has engaged in some mild self injurious behavior (hitting and scratching) and she appears to be purging in an attempt to regulate mood and not for weight loss purposes. All of these factors may suggest BPD, however, further evaluation reveals her relationships to be stable and that generally she functions quite well.

A number of other diagnosis should be considered. An eating disorder is suggested both by her vomiting and appearance although she denies body image concerns or attempts to lose weight. Depression must be ruled out as there are some mild depressive symptoms (sleep disturbance and anhedonia) as well as family history of depression. In addition, she is described as a "perfectionist" and this should be further defined in order to rule out Obsessive-Compulsive Personality Disorder or Obsessive-Compulsive Disorder.

However, in this case, diagnostic criteria was not met for any of these disorders. Further evaluation revealed fairly severe situational stressors that suggested that these behaviors were most appropriately categorized as part of an Adjustment Disorder. Further, she was referred for a medical evaluation which revealed a medical condition contributing to her vomiting. (Hyperthyroidism and/or pregnancy would be suggested by her symptoms). This case illustrates the importance of thorough medical evaluation as medical causes may also explain symptomatic behaviors especially when they are a change from previous functioning.

Case Scenario #3: Client is a 38-year-old mother of two who presented at the emergency room. Her husband came home and found her passed out with empty pill bottles by the bed. This is her third suicide attempt in the past six months. He stated he had been worried about her lately as she had been increasingly moody and depressed. He reported he has caught her sitting in her room burning herself with cigarettes and "just staring into space." "I don't understand it. Nothing like this has ever happened before.

She's been so moody. Doesn't want anything to do with me. Accuses me of having affairs. Says I should just leave her. It's like someone else has moved into our home."

He described her as having become more and more withdrawn since her daughter's tenth birthday party. He reported she has been having increasing nightmares and had just recently shared with him that she had been sexually abused by her uncle as a child.

On the surface this client is exhibiting many of the diagnostic criteria for BPD including self injurious behavior, dissociation, mood lability, irritability, and possible paranoia ("She accuses me of having affairs."). However, she does not meet criteria for BPD because the pervasiveness criterion is not met, and these symptoms were not present prior to early adulthood.

In this case these symptoms are evidence of an acute exacerbation of PTSD. In addition, she is experiencing nightmares which are more consistent with a PTSD diagnosis. It is likely that something about here daughter's 10th birthday or the party served as a trigger for intrusive thoughts regarding her abuse.

It is my experience that abuse victims often experience an acute exacerbation of PTSD symptoms when their child or grandchild reaches the age they were when abused. Often they are misdiagnosed because their behavior looks like Borderline Behavior. However, it does not meet the age of onset and prevalence criteria and thus a diagnosis of BPD is inappropriate.

Case Scenario #4: Client is a 25-year-old female who presents in the emergency room after passing out at a party due to alcohol intoxication. There is suggestion, although unconfirmed, that she may have been sexually assaulted. Toxicology screening indicates alcohol use and the presence of a drug commonly seen in date rape cases.

Upon regaining consciousness the client indicates that she went to the party to try to talk to a guy she had been dating as she was concerned he had gone there to see another girl. She brought him an expensive gift and attempted to convince him to continue dating her. When he ignored her she began drinking and flirting openly with other men in an attempt to make him jealous. When he didn't respond she became distraught. She threw his gift in the pool, screamed profanities at him, and continued drinking heavi-

> ly. She last recalls "talking to this really sweet guy about the whole thing" and then waking up in the hospital. She denies the possibility he could have assaulted her stating, "It had to be someone else. He wasn't like that. He just listened to me. He was the nicest guy I've ever met."
>
> She acknowledges she likes "to party" but denies symptoms of alcohol dependence. She has burns on her thighs which she states are cigarette burns "that help me calm down." She does not want family called stating, "They all hate me and think it's my fault anyway." She states she can't stay in treatment as "it's too expensive." She doesn't have health insurance since she abruptly quit her job after a fight with a co-worker. "I didn't really like that job anyway. I just don't know what I want to do with my life."

Again, this client quite clearly exhibits many of the diagnostic criteria for BPD. She attempts to avoid the rejection of a man by buying him gifts and flirting with other men then becomes distraught when he doesn't respond. She idealizes the young man she spoke to, dismissing the possibility he may have harmed her even though she knows little about him. She engages in self injurious behaviors (cigarette burns) and impulsive self damaging behaviors (drinking, flirtation, and possibly quitting work). She appears to have an unstable or conflictual relationship with her family and possibly with co-workers. Feelings of emptiness and/or unstable identity may also be indicated by her last statement.

What is unknown here is the pervasiveness of this kind of behavior. If this is a short term change from her usual functioning an Adjustment Disorder or Chemical Abuse diagnosis should be ruled out. If this is an established pervasive pattern the BPD diagnosis may be appropriate. Historical information regarding her functioning and prior treatment is necessary to make this distinction.

CHAPTER SUMMARY

In summary, these case studies illustrate the complexity in diagnosis and yet the relatively consistent patterns of concerns for clients with BPD. While the term Borderline is a historical one without much current relevance, the term identifies a pattern of instability of emotions, behavior, relationships and cognitive functioning.

The disorder tends to be more common in women especially in early adulthood and does improve over time.

Specific DSM-IV criteria identify the disorder but these must be present by early adulthood and be pervasive in nature. Given this, the best assessment tool is a thorough history taking which covers many aspects of functioning. Diagnostic overlap, along with high rates of comorbidity make differential diagnosis difficult. When in doubt, the clinician should consider key distinguishing factors and should also consider whether or not further diagnostic clarification is really necessary to inform treatment. Given the stigma attached to the Borderline diagnosis it may be best to minimize its use unless absolutely certain.

3

Understanding the Etiology of the Disorder

Having come to some understanding of the diagnostic criteria and what this disorder looks like one can move to an understanding of what precipitates the development of this pervasive pattern of behaviors. While multiple theories of etiology exist most agree that there is no single pathway to the development of this disorder (Zanarini, 1997; Zelkowitz, Paris, & Feldman, 2001). In fact there seem to be multiple factors contributing to its development. However, theorists generally agree upon three primary causes involved in the development of BPD: biological vulnerability, environment, and history of trauma.

Theorists agree there seems to be some biological though not necessarily genetic vulnerability to this condition. BPD is about five times more common among first-degree biological relatives of those with the disorder but it is impossible to determine to what extent this is due to genetics and to what extent it is due to environment (Dean, 2001). Linehan (1993) argues there is a biological vulnerability which may or may not be genetic. She postulates that other factors such as interuterine trauma, nutrition, chemical use or other toxins, psychological or physical trauma, and/or chance may play a role in the development of the central nervous system resulting in a biological difficulty in regulating emotions. Other theorists have argued that BPD is a variant of the affective disorders spectrum and have looked for similar biological markers. To date such findings have been highly inconsistent. Biological factors and theories in BPD are further discussed in Chapter 4.

Environment also appears to play a significant role in the development of BPD. Backgrounds of those with BPD are often chaotic, unstable, contradictory or abusive. There are high rates of familial breakdown and parental criminality for clients with BPD (Guzder, Paris, Zelkowitz, & Feldman, 1999). Linehan (1993) refers to these environmental factors as an "invalidating environment." This concept discussed later in this chapter.

Often these unstable environments include a history of trauma. The majority of people with BPD (about 90%) have experienced significantly higher rates of childhood trauma than non-BPD clients (Dean, 2001). This may take the form of physical (71%) or sexual (68%) abuse or as witnessing domestic violence (62%). BPD occurs significantly more often in women reporting early-onset abuse than those reporting late onset abuse. Parental sexual abuse is strongly correlated with suicidal behavior in Borderlines, and both parental sexual abuse and emotional neglect are significantly related to self-mutilation (Dubo, Zanarini, Lewis, & Williams, 1997). Further, Borderlines experience significantly higher rates of violence as adults (Zanarini, et al., 1999).

DIALECTIC BEHAVIORAL THEORY REGARDING THE ETIOLOGY OF BPD

Currently, Dialectic Behavioral Therapy (DBT) is the treatment of choice for clients with BPD. Like other theoretical approaches to the etiology of BPD, DBT considers biological and environmental factors including trauma in the development of BPD. Also like other theories it acknowledges that there may be many pathways to the disorder. However, DBT's view of etiology emphasizes the role of these factors in the development (or lack thereof) of emotion regulation skills and views the primary "problem" in BPD as emotion dysregulation.

Throughout her work, Linehan (1993, 1995) argues that individuals with BPD have a "biological predisposition to emotion dysregulation." Again, she postulates that such a biological predisposition may be due to a number of factors including genetics, interuterine trauma, nutrition, toxins, psychological or physical trauma, or chance.

What is emotion dysregulation? Linehan identifies it as a combination of "emotional vulnerability" and an "inability to modulate emotions." Our emotional vulnerability has to do with our physiological and psychological response to stimuli. Persons who are emotionally vulnerable are highly sensitive to environmental stimuli. In other words, they are easily moved or upset by things. In addition to being sensitive, those who are emotionally vulnerable are highly reactive. In other words, when they feel something they feel it strongly. In part this is because they have strong physiological reactions to stimuli. Finally, they have a slow return to baseline, meaning it takes them longer to lower their level of arousal and calm down.

We all have varying levels of sensitivity and reactivity to emotional stimuli. Some of us stay excited about things for some time, others of us easily become subdued. On the one extreme are individuals who "wear their heart on their sleeve." It is quickly obvious to others how they are feeling. On the other extreme are those we might describe as "stoic" or even "robotic." They show little emotion regardless of the situation.

Since I do a great deal of traveling and speaking I often think about this in relationship to temperature controls. It never fails that a number of people in the workshop complain about the room being too hot and an equal number complain about it being too cold. Sometimes I can alter the thermostat only slightly and the temperature changes dramatically. Other times we can "crank it up" and nothing happens. Different thermostats have different levels of sensitivity and reactivity. One room may hold the temperature very constant while another is highly variable. Some individuals are happy with only minor changes in the room and others continue to shiver. Different rooms have different sensitivity, reactivity and return to baseline rates in response to changes in the thermostat. Likewise, different individuals have different sensitivity, reactivity and return to baseline rates in response to changes in the room temperature. Borderline's "emotional thermostat" is highly sensitive and reactive but once "cranked up" it is difficult to get them calmed back down.

In addition to emotional vulnerability, Linehan argues that Borderlines have difficulty with "emotion modulation." Emotion modulation refers to how we get from one emotional state to another. In other words, if I get angry with my spouse in the morning but I'm calm by lunch—what happened in between? For most of us this happens naturally and without much thought. However, Linehan argues Borderlines have difficulty making these emotional transitions and have to be taught the skills necessary to do so.

So, how does one change one's feelings? According to Linehan (1993) there are four tasks to emotion modulation including: 1) Increasing or Decreasing the physiological arousal associated with emotion; 2) Reorienting attention; 3) Inhibiting mood dependent action; and 4) Organizing one's behavior in the service of non-mood dependent goals.

First, one must decrease the physiological arousal associated with emotion. When I am angry, my heart and respiration rates are likely high, I may have muscle tension in my face and shoulder, I may even clench my fists, speak rapidly and loudly, etc. These are all manifestations of my physiological arousal. In order to change my mood I must be able to lower my blood pressure, loosen my muscles, quiet and slow my voice, etc. Again, in most of us this happens quite naturally but for those who are highly sensitive, reactive, and have a slow return to baseline this process may take longer and be more difficult.

Second, I must reorient my attention. In other words, I have to be able to stop attending to the original emotional stimuli and pay attention to something else. If I leave angry at my spouse in the morning and think about our argument all the way to work I am likely to stay angry, but if I listen to the radio or begin planning for work I am likely to become less angry. If I think about positive aspects of the relationship my feelings of anger may even begin to be replaced by feelings of love and compassion.

Lastly, one must be able to "inhibit mood dependent action and organize behavior in the service of non-mood dependent goals." Put simply, one has to NOT do what you FEEL like doing and do what's in your best interest regardless of how you feel. Most of us at one point are so angry we feel like choking someone. Fortunately few of us do it! We have learned to inhibit our mood dependent response. Initially, I was very nervous about presenting in front of the group and literally had the urge to run out of the room. I had to force myself to walk to the front of the room, take out my materials, and begin talking to the group. I eventually become less nervous and even somewhat confident.

The problem for Borderlines is that they are biologically "wired" to have difficulty with these tasks. Thus, they are often seen as "moody," "stubborn," "dramatic" and over-reactive." In fact, they are highly sensitive individuals with strong, passionate feelings who have difficulty managing and changing those feelings. The problem is emotion dysregulation.

Obviously, not everyone who has these emotional characteristics becomes Borderline. According to Linehan (1993) there is a second critical element to the etiology—"an invalidating environment." According to Dialectic Behavioral Theory "an invalidating environment invalidates behavior and/or identity independent of the actual validity of the behavior or identity." In other words, it says "Your behavior, feelings, or person are not important or okay as they are." Linehan (1993, 1995) states that an invalidating environment does three things. It: 1) indiscriminately rejects communications of private experiences and behaviors; 2) punishes emotional displays and intermittently reinforces emotional escalation; and 3) oversimplifies the ease of solving problems and meeting goals.

In other words, the emotionally vulnerable individual says "I'm very upset." or begins to cry. The environment responds in words or actions in such a manner that says, "I don't know what you're upset about." "It's not that big of a deal." "Stop your crying." "You're over-reacting." etc. In cases of the neglectful home, the cries might simply be ignored.

Think about the last time you were very upset or angry and someone told you, "Calm down. It's not that big of a deal!"—Didn't that only make you more upset? Did you start to feel "crazy" and like you either couldn't trust your own experience or couldn't trust others to understand you?

Worse yet, the emotional displays may be punished, "I'm not going to talk to you if you're going to be like that!" "Stop crying or I'm going to spank you!" or "I'll give you something to cry about." At other times they may be rewarded, "Here have a piece of candy that'll shut you up." "You poor thing, if you stop crying I'll take you for ice cream."

How does the invalidating environment oversimplify problem solving? One way this happens is by expecting the child to be able to do things they are yet incapable of. Have you ever witnessed a parent asking a child to do something that is clearly not age appropriate (e.g. A parent spanking a two year old for not sitting perfectly still.) Imagine the frustration this causes for the individual who is emotionally sensitive!

The second way the environment may oversimplify problem solving is by underestimating the difficulty of doing something given the individuals emotional state. Have you ever tried to do something while you were really upset? If physiologically aroused you may have found yourself dropping things or otherwise feeling clumsy. You may have had difficulty concentrating or carrying out step by step instructions. It is difficult to complete tasks when we are in a highly charged emotional state. Borderlines, because of their emotional dysregulation are often in a highly charged state making carrying out day to day tasks difficult. Thus, the environment says "What's the matter with you? This is easy." when it is not at all easy for them.

Linehan proposes that the invalidating environment leads to chronic problems in emotion regulation in which the individual learns to actively invalidate themselves, oscillate between emotional inhibition and extreme emotional styles, and form unrealistic goals and expectations.

Invalidating Environments teach an individual to ignore their own internal responses and search the environment for cues as to how to respond. In other words, when a child grows up in an environment that communicates to them "There's something wrong with you. You get too upset," the child learns not to trust their own feelings and instead to look to others for "appropriate reactions." Often Borderlines describe this as follows, "I don't know who I am. When I'm in a group I just watch everyone else and see how they are reacting." Over time, they may actually lose touch with their true feelings. Linehan (1993, 1995) indicates that this phenomenon accounts for their feelings of emptiness and lack of identity. It is difficult to develop a sense of self when you are looking to others to know how you should feel about things!

Further, this leads clients to try to shut down their emotional reactions which they perceive as untrustworthy (emotional inhibition). Of course no one can persistently shut down their feelings, and this is especially difficult for those who are emotionally vulnerable. As a result they have episodes of dramatic emotional outbursts. The result is a vacillation between emotional inhibition and extreme emotional displays.

Finally, the invalidating environment leads the Borderline to form unrealistic goals and expectations for themselves. Because others seem to think things are easy they assume they should be easy for them. However the Borderline individual does not possess the emotion regulation skills that would make such tasks easier.

Linehan argues that this combination of poor emotion regulation skills along with the invalidating environment leads to chronic emotion dysregulation. This she states is the etiology of BPD.

Table 2: DBT's Biopsychosocial Theory of Etiology (Linehan, 1993)

A biological dysfunction in the emotion regulation system

plus

An invalidating environment

leads to . . .

Pervasive Emotion Dysregulation

It is important to note that while it is believed to be a combination of these factors, each factor may contribute to varying degrees. For example a child with relatively good emotion regulation skills if placed in an extremely abusive and chaotic home may develop BPD. Likewise a child with very poor emotion regulation skills may develop BPD even with a relatively intact home.

This is important to note as historically the field has sometimes taken a "blame the parent" approach which has not only been unhelpful but at times destructive. It is important to understand that the emotionally vulnerable child may elicit a less validating approach in parents who may otherwise be caring and compassionate parents. These children, who might be described as "difficult to sooth," require a strong balance of nurturing, validation, and limit setting. They may be more difficult to parent in some ways and be even more likely to elicit an abusive response from a parent who is already so inclined.

I once saw a young woman who had a history of mild self injury including banging her head and scratching herself as well as some other mild symptoms suggestive of problems regulating her mood. At least one of her siblings had been diagnosed with depression and all her siblings had engaged in some occasional mild form of cutting, scratching, or head banging when upset. Family history did not reveal a history of divorce, abuse, or other trauma. In fact by all accounts this was an extremely loving and supportive family. My client did not meet criteria for borderline personality disorder.but one wonders if there was some biological tendency toward emotional dysregulation in these children that was somewhat tempered by a supportive environment. If these children hadbeen raised in an abusive, chaotic environment it is possible they may have developed BPD.

Linehan (1993, 1995) argues that the diagnostic criterion behaviors are either a direct result of these pervasive problems in emotion regulation or are an attempt to regulate emotions. In other words, Borderlines act in impulsive ways either because they can't inhibit their mood dependent reaction or in an effort to change their feelings.

For example, the borderline who becomes angry with a significant other has all kinds of negative thoughts about him come into her head. She is unable to control her impulse and screams a string of insults at her husband ending with "Just get the hell out!" When she calms down she becomes distraught because she doesn't really want to end the relationship. She may become very anxious and agitated and decide to "just have a few drinks to calm me down" or go on a shopping spree "because it makes me feel better." Likewise, when a client becomes overwhelmed with anxiety or dysphoria she may begin to have paranoid like thinking or dissociate as a way to escape her painful emotions. She may even view suicide as the ultimate means of ending her emotional discomfort. Thus, the criterion behaviors are a symptom of the ultimate problem, difficulty regulating emotions. It follows that treatment must primarily revolve around aiding the client in regulating her own emotions.

CHAPTER SUMMARY

In summary, there are many theories regarding the etiology of BPD and all agree there seem to be multiple pathways to this disorder. Most theories agree that the disorder seems to arise from some combination of three factors: 1) Biological and/or Genetic Vulnerability; 2) Unstable or Invalidating Environments; and 3) A History of Trauma and/or Abuse. DBT argues that this disorder is primarily due to a pervasive pattern of emotion dysregulation which develops because of some combination of a biological predisposition to emotional vulnerability and difficulty modulating affect, and an invalidating environment. Criterion behaviors are thus either an attempt to regulate emotions or a result of the failed ability to do so.

4

The Biological Struggle: Understanding the Neurobiology of Borderline Personality Disorder

As indicated in the previous chapter, DBT postulates that individuals with BPD suffer from a biological vulnerability to difficulty in regulating emotions. This hypothesis begs a number of questions including: 1) What evidence is there of biological dysfunction and specifically central nervous system dysfunction in clients with BPD? 2) What causes such dysfunction? and 3) What are the clinical implications of any such findings?

Evidence for biological dysfunction in BPD can be found in neuropsychological test results, brain imaging studies, and chemical analysis of individuals with BPD. However, to date many of these findings are preliminary and must be replicated in further studies.

NEUROPSYCHOLOGICAL TEST FINDINGS

While there are consistent clinical reports of cognitive and perceptual problems in clients with BPD, there are limited studies to date that evaluate neurocognitive functioning of Borderlines. Those that do exist often result in conflicting findings. Studies of Weschler Adult Intelligence Scale (WAIS) scores in persons with BPD have indicated greater intra- and inter-test scatter, odd word usage, and lapses in logical thinking on tasks requiring the extensive use of language (Judd & Ruff, 1993). Other studies have found deficits on memory tests requiring uncued recall of complex, recently learned material and on tasks measuring visuospatial discrimination, speed, and fluency (Judd & Ruff, 1993). These findings suggest Borderlines experience a dysfunction in learning new complex information.

BRAIN IMAGING AND CHEMICAL FINDINGS

Problems in memory functions are further supported by findings of brain imaging and chemical studies which show abnormalities in the portions of the brain associated with memory. At least one study has found reduced Hippocampal and Amygdala volumes in clients with BPD (Schmahl, C. G., Vermetten, E., Elzinga, B. & Bremner, J., 2003). The amygdala is the portion of the brain which controls the fight or flight response. Thus, dysfunction in this area may lead to very strong emotional memories which bypass the more cognitive influence. The result is a client who reacts rapidly and instinctively with fear, aggression or depression. The hippocampus is involved in memory functions which, as previously discussed, seemed to be impaired in BPD. The clinical implications for these findings are discussed elsewhere in this chapter.

In this study patients with BPD had a 21.9 percent smaller mean amygdala volume and a 13.1 percent smaller hippocampal volume as compared to controls. However, it should be noted that other studies have indicated similar findings in individuals who have been traumatized. Given the high rate of trauma for persons with BPD one must question whether it is the trauma that is associated with lowered hippocampal and amygdala volumes, the BPD itself, or both. Thus, these findings should be confirmed by replication and by further studies which compare Borderlines with traumatic histories to those without traumatic histories. Nonetheless, given the high rate of trauma in persons with BPD, these findings lend support to the notion of a biological vulnerability to difficulty with regulating emotions and memory. In this case, this biological vulnerability would seem to be due to the neurobiological effects of trauma.

In addition, at least one study of Borderline clients has found significant hypometabolism in the hippocampus and cuneus (Juengling, F., et al, 2003) using Positron emission tomography (PET). Again this would indicate a negative impact on memory functioning. Further, Juengling et al (2003) also found hypermetabolism in frontal and prefrontal cortex which confirms other studies which suggest problems in the frontal and temporal lobes (Ajamieh & Ansseau, 2000). Such findings of limbic and prefrontal dysfunction support the notion of biological dysfunction in emotion regulation as this network of brain regions has been implicated in the regulation of emotion. The frontal and prefrontal regions are also thought to be involved in impulse control and social judgement which again are areas in which persons with BPD experience dysfunction.

There are also biochemical findings which show abnormalities in the Borderlines ability to regulate negative affect. Studies indicate that Borderlines with affective instability respond to physostigmine (a cholinesterase inhibitor which prevents the breakdown of acetylcholine) with marked feelings of negative mood and/or dysphoria while patients with other personality disorders and a normal control group showed no such response (Sievers, 1997). Thus, abnormalities in the cholinergic system may also be involved in mediating the dysphoric symptoms of BPD.

Further, reductions in serotonergic activity has been associated with impulsive and aggressive behaviors. Persons with BPD, as well as individuals with antisocial personality disorder, demonstrate a blunted prolactin response to fefluramine (a serotonin releasing agent) thus suggesting that the serotonergic system may be involved in Borderlines and other clients with impulsive and aggressive behaviors (Sievers, 1997).

FACTORS AFFECTING NEUROBIOLOGICAL DEVELOPMENT

GENETICS/TEMPERAMENT

While there is some suggestion that BPD may be influenced by genetic factors most research suggest that it is the characteristics of emotional reactivity and impulsive aggression that are heritable (Kernberg, et al, 2000). These biological vulnerabilities are expressed in the individuals "temperament." Temperament refers to the individual's inborn and constitutional differences in the automatic response of the individual to emotional or affect-laden stimuli.

Studies indicate a five times greater incidence of BPD in first degree relatives of Borderlines (Dean, 2001) however it is not clear to what degree this is heredity and to what degree it is environment.

To determine this one would have to find a significant number of identical twins, separated at birth and raised in different environments, who developed BPD and who are able and willing to participate in an extensive study. Thus, this research is impractical.

Genetic studies of monozygotic and dizygotic twins do suggest that there may be genetic factors for emotional reactivity and impulsive aggression while there does not appear to be a specific heritability for BPD (Sievers, 1997; White, Gunderson, Zanarini, & Hudson, 2003). Blunted prolactin response to fenfluramine in an individual is a better predictor of impulsivity and aggression in their relatives than impulsive aggression itself in the patient (Sievers, 1997). This would indicate that what is inherited is an alteration in setonergic functioning that may be expressed as a vulnerability to impulsive aggression. This notion is supported by the relatively favorable response to Specific Serotonin Reuptake Inhibitors (SSRI's) in individuals with impulse control problems.

ATTACHMENT

In addition to these genetic or inborn tendencies, the brain undergoes life long changes in its neural connections. However, research supports that the brain is especially vulnerable to the development of particular neural pathways during the birth to three years. Thus, one is particularly vulnerable to the role environmental factors in neurodevelopment during these years. In particular, attachment and trauma seem to play a role in the biological vulnerability in BPD.

For a complete discussion of the neurophysiology of attachment the reader is referred to the writings of Kernberg et al, (2000) which are briefly summarized here. There is a growing body of evidence that early caregiver infant attachment plays a critical role in neurodevelopment. During face-to face interactions with the child, the caregiver's gaze has the effect of stimulating cortocotropin releasing factor (CRF) in the infant's paraventricular hypothalamus. This in turn increases plasma noradrenaline levels resulting in emotional excitement. When the mother and child are well attuned such interactions elicit rapid neural activity associated with imprinting, rapid learning, and formation of attachment bonds.

During this time the brain also undergoes the selective loss of synapses and dendritic connections in pathways which are not used. Also at this time amygdala is dominant in shaping the infants emotional life. By the end of the first year the orbito-insular region of the prefrontal cortex (the area of the brain which responds to faces) develops as the mother's facial expressions guide the infant's behavior. During this time the slightest change in the mother's affect can cause dramatic shifts in the infants affect and subsequent development of neural pathways.

In negative mother-infant situations the infant loses the ability to overcome negative affects. In this way disturbed parent-child relationships create a biological vulnerability to despair and depression. Excessively high cortisol levels in the infant inhibit dendritic branching leading to destruction in the limbic system and to permanent impairment in the child's ability to regulate emotions.

Well attuned mothers may mediate any constitutional difficulties the child may have in these regions by providing optimal bonding experiences. Unfortunately, children with strong genetic loading for negative affect or problems with impulse control, sometimes referred to as "difficult to soothe" infants, may alienate mothers who would otherwise have the potential for attunement and nurturing. In other words, such children tend to elicit negative affective responses in the caregiver which only reinforces the neural pathways for negative affect.

TRAUMA

As previously noted a large percentage of Borderlines report a history of trauma. Recent research indicates that abuse may cause chemical and structural changes in the brain which may lead to ongoing biological vulnerabilities. Traumatic experiences, especially if severe and sustained, lead to cell damage and premature death in key centers of the brain (Kernberg et al, 2000). This results in wiring patterns that trigger maladaptive responses to ordinary events in life. Such neural pathways are difficult if not impossible to reverse. Studies also suggest that abuse may alter the activity of the stress system and cause structural changes in the hippocampus and amygdala. As previously indicated theses are the emotional memory centers of the brain (Sievers, 1997).

CLINICAL IMPLICATIONS OF NEUROBIOLOGICAL FINDINGS

While these neuropsychological and neurobiological findings are interesting in and of themselves, they are useless unless they can be translated in clinical implications and interventions.

For example, if the Borderline client experiences dysfunction in encoding or learning new complex information how may this effect them? Judd & Ruff (1993) argue that such cognitive deficits make it difficult for the client to learn from interpersonal situations and to articulate complex emotional information. This creates difficulty in developing coherent interpersonal and affective schemas. In that sense they may remain in the preoperational phase in terms of their cognitive-affective development. Therapy then must focus on helping clients reach formal operations in the interpersonal area.

This would include assisting the client in constructing an integrated understanding of their behavior, emotions and interpersonal situations. The therapist would help the client translate their behavior into an abstract understanding of their social role and emotions and the other persons role and context. As will be discussed later in this text, this is consistent with DBT techniques such as behavioral chain analysis and interpersonal skills training.

Second, if the memory centers of the brain are damaged and thus, Borderlines have difficulty learning new complex information, it may make it more difficult for them to learn new skills or behavior. While most of us benefit from trial and error learning the Borderline client may have more difficulty benefiting from such experience or organizing the information learned. As a result, they tend to make the same errors in cognition or behavior over and over again. This is especially true in affectively charged interpersonal situations as the anxiety and distress may further impact their concentration and memory abilities. The result is that it takes them much longer to learn new skills and behaviors. This can add to the caregiver's frustration at the seemingly unwillingness or inability to change. Caregiver's often become exasperated stating "When will she ever learn?" and these responses only add to the Borderline's shame and feelings of rejection. By understanding that the individual with BPD has to overcome neurological deficits to learn this information rather than assuming ill intent, the caregiver may learn to be more patient and empathic.

Third, if the memory center of the brain is impaired clients may fail to encode information that most of us would remember. As a result they may not recall critical information or incidents. When asked about such incidents they may say "I'd never do that!" or "I don't remember." Too often professionals and loved ones misattribute such comments and assume the client is "lying," "defensive," "in denial" or "being manipulative." This then sets up a power struggle to get the client to "admit to" the behavior. This is rarely beneficial and usually only further alienates the client and frustrates the caregiver. Instead of debating "what happened" it may be more beneficial to move on to a "what now" approach. This is not to say that clients with BPD never lie but rather that this lack of memory is too often ascribed malicious intent when it may in fact be a result of neurological impairment.

Finally, these findings would indicate that the Borderline client's tendency to "over-react" or react inappropriately to certain situations may be the result of neurological damage to the emotional memory centers of the brain. As a result the borderlines neurological system may react to relatively minor stressors with an extreme fight or flight response or dissociative reactions. Again, this can often be misinterpreted and ascribed malicious intent. "She's being dramatic again!" Instead we must understand that these reactions are a result of strongly imprinted neural pathways which are easily triggered but not necessarily appropriate to the situation.

If we assume this to be true then the client may be incapable of higher order reasoning when in such a hyperaroused state. The client may need assistance in lowering her state of arousal and interventions aimed at doing so must occur before the client can "be reasonable" about the situation.

CHAPTER SUMMARY

Neuropsychological testing, brain imaging studies, and chemical findings all support structural and chemical neurological dysfunction in BPD. Such dysfunction includes hypometabolism and lowered volume in the hypocampal and amygdala regions, hypermetabolism in the frontal and prefrontal region and abnormalities in the cholinergic and sertonergic systems. Such neurological impairment may be a result of genetics, poor attachment, trauma or other biological factors. These deficits lead to problems in emotion regulation, an exaggerated fight or flight response, poor higher order reasoning, memory deficits, and problems in impulse control. By understanding that these symptoms are a result of biological dysfunction and not intentional on the client's part the caregiver may by more understanding and effective in their interventions.

5

The Struggle to Stay Alive

For many Borderlines, one of the biggest struggles is chronic thoughts of suicide or other self harm. It is difficult to focus on other goals in life when one is chronically overwhelmed with urges to hurt oneself. Likewise for many clinicians one of the biggest struggles is dealing with the client's chronic parasuidical behavior. It is difficult to focus on other therapeutic goals or set limits when one is worried about the client's safety. This anxiety can often lead to countertransference reactions in the clinicians including feelings of hopelessness, helplessness, anger, and resentment.

I have found it critical for clinicians to develop confidence in their ability to assess and intervene with regard to these behaviors. Such behaviors create risks (client's death, law suit) which ultimately raise the clinician's anxiety making it difficult to focus on the tasks at hand. Because we think less clearly when anxious, it is important to gain confidence to minimize our anxiety. In addition it is important to over-learn strategies related to risk assessment because we tend to remember things that have been overlearned better when anxious. For this reason, strong training in risk assessment and intervention is a critical first step in treating clients with BPD.

PARASUICIDAL BEHAVIOR IN BPD

It should be noted that the same kinds of assessment, intervention, and documentation skills are needed whether the client is at risk for harming others, intends to commit suicide, or is engaging in self-injurious behavior without suicidal intent. In any of these circumstances, risk is present but the intervention may vary depending on the behavior and the client's intent. Regardless of intent, behavior aimed at harming oneself is referred to as "parasuicidal behavior." Parasuicide is defined as *"any intentional, acute, self-injurious behavior with or without suicidal intent, including both suicide attempts and self-mutilating behaviors."* (Linehan, 1993).

Note that the behavior must be intentionally self injurious and acute. In other words, chronically driving too fast, talking on one's cellular phone, and crossing lanes into oncoming traffic is risky behavior but would not be considered parasuicidal behavior because it is unintentional and likely chronic rather than acute. On the other hand, an individual who is driving and talking on her cell phone, has an argument, becomes distraught, decides to commit suicide and pulls into oncoming traffic is engaging in parasuicidal behavior. Crossing the center line into oncoming traffic with the intent of killing oneself would be considered parasuicidal behavior because it is intentional and acute.

People often ask if behaviors such as tattooing or piercing should be considered parasuicidal behaviors. In most cases they are not because the intent is not to injure oneself but to decorate oneself. Many teens may engage in what appears on the surface to be self-injurious behavior (self piercing, tattooing, cutting) but upon exploration of their motives such behavior is intended to be "cool" or make them part of a group and not as self-inflicted punishment. Thus, one must look at the motive underlying such behavior as well as its "subcultural" context. If the intent of the behavior is to harm, punish, or otherwise injure oneself it is likely parasuicidal. If it is to decorate oneself, "see what it's like," be part of a group, or is otherwise part of a subcultural ritual it most likely should not be considered parasuicidal behavior. Nonetheless it is risky behavior that must be addressed but it would not necessarily qualify under diagnostic criteria 5 for BPD.

As previously stated, BPD is the only disorder for which parasuicidal behavior is listed in the diagnostic criteria but not everyone who engages in parasuicidal behavior is borderline. Likewise not all Borderlines self injure. However, 69 to 80 % of clients with BPD have a history of at least one parasuicidal act (Dean, 2001; Fine & Sansone, 1990; Schroeder, Oster-Granite, & Thompson, 2002). As a comparison, the prevalence of self injury in a general psychiatric population is estimated at 4 percent (Schroeder, Oster-Granite, & Thompson, 2002).

Studies consistently estimate the percentage of Borderlines who complete suicide at 3 to 10% (Fine & Sansone,1990; Dean, 2001;

Paris. 2002) and most completed suicides happen later in the course of the illness (Paris, 2002). This reiterates the importance of clinicians dealing with borderlines having adequate understanding of risk assessment, intervention, and documentation techniques. In short, Borderlines are more likely to self injure than other psychiatric populations but not necessarily more likely to complete suicide.

FUNCTIONS OF PARASUICIDAL BEHAVIOR

One of the most critical points to understand in dealing with parasuicidal behavior is that while helping professionals and others tend to view parasuicidal behavior as a "problem," borderlines view it as a "solution." This is extremely important because unless the clinician and client agree on what the "problem" is, they will often be working at cross purposes. Most often, professionals simply want the client with BPD to stop the self-injurious behavior and become frustrated when the client seems unable or even unwilling to do so. Often this is misinterpreted to mean they "enjoy" the behavior.

Invariably if one explores this sufficiently one finds that the reason they are unable or unwilling to stop self injury it not that they truly or completely believe self injury is in their best interest but because they view it as the only or the most efficient means to meeting some need. If one explores the thoughts, urges, and feelings associated with the parasuicidal behavior sufficiently one can identify what functions it serves (i.e. what the "problem" is for the client) and can then teach the client less damaging strategies to serve that function or meet that need.

Notice I use the term "less damaging" and not "more efficient" or "more effective." This choice of wording is intentional as part of what the client may have to learn is that they may need to use other strategies that in fact are more difficult or take longer to be effective than self injury. Part of the intervention then is to convince them to choose a strategy that ultimately may be more difficult but is less damaging.

So how does parasuicidal behavior serve to solve problems? Parasuicidal behavior has multiple purposes but I have found it usually tends to serve one of the following five functions: 1) Emotion Regulation; 2) Communication; 3)Relief from dissociation; 4) Relief from racing or obsessive thoughts; and 5) Maintaining a sense of control (especially control of pain or of their bodies). These functions are summarized in Table 3 and will be explained in some detail here.

Table 3 Functions of Parasuicidal Behavior

1. Emotion Regulation—"I feel better afterward."
2. Communication—"They wouldn't listen so I decided to show them."
3. Relief from Dissociation—"It's the only way I feel real."
4. Relief from Racing or Obsessive Thoughts—"I have all these thoughts going through my head and it's the only way to make them stop."
5. Control of Pain—"I can't control the feelings but I can control that."

PARASUICIDAL BEHAVIOR AS A MEANS OF REGULATING EMOTIONS

"Implicit among the various explanations and theoretical frames is the simple notion that borderline patients engage in SIB (self-injurious behavior) in order to *feel better*" (Kemperman, Russ, & Shearin, 1997). In a study of individuals who engage in self-injurious behavior, self mutilators reported that parasuicidal behavior helps them to feel more relaxed (65%), feel less depressed (58%), and feel less lonely (47%) (Favazza & Conterio, 1989). Kemperman, Russ, & Shearin (1997) found that in particular Borderlines report a change in levels of anger after self injury and that anger tends to be the emotion with the most dramatic decrease. When asked how they felt immediately after injury 66% reported feeling better, 13% reported no change, and 21% reported feeling worse (Favazza & Conterio, 1989). These percentages tended to reverse as time passed after the self injury. These findings can be helpful in intervening with Borderlines as they illustrate that while they may feel better immediately it does not elicit long term emotional relief and in fact may ultimately make them feel worse.

How is it that parasuicidal behavior makes clients feel better? Linehan's biosocial theory of BPD (Linehan, 1993) as previously discussed provides a learning theory model to explain parasuicidal behavior in clients with BPD. This model as applied to parasuicidal behavior holds that these individuals have difficulty regulating their emotions in combination with an invalidating environment. They learn self injury to regulate their emotions both because of the direct biological effects of self injury as well as other reinforcing properties such at attention, support, nurturance and avoidance of unpleasant situations. Other theorists suggest that self injurious behavior is an auto addictive process. This view suggests that self-injurious behavior elevates levels of endogenous opiates requiring repetition to maintain the resulting "high."

The direct biological effects of self-injurious behavior are not fully understood but biological hypothesis tend to emphasize the impulsive and aggressive aspects of parasuicidal behavior implicating central serotonergic dysfunction and mood regulating functions implicating both central serotonergic and edogenous opioid systems. (See Chapter 4 for further information on the neurobiology of BPD). Put simply, when one cuts oneself accidentally or on purpose, the body's automatic neurochemical response is to release pain killers and sedatives. Thus, self injurious behaviors (as well as vomiting) likely cause a surge in the body's natural pain killers including the natural opiates and serotonin. Both are known to reduce anxiety and increase positive affect. This immediate physiological response serves to calm the Borderline's sensitive and reactive system and helps them more quickly return to a neutral or positive affect.

Unfortunately self injurious behaviors are then paired with this calming response. Just as in relaxation training the relaxation response can be paired with other behavioral or environmental cues, rituals around the self injury may become paired with the physiological calming response. Unfortunately this further reinforces the behaviors associated with self injury. As a result clients will often develop elaborate rituals of self injury such as keeping a special box of items for use in self injury. As will be discussed later, this pairing must be broken as part of teaching the clients other skills or may be used to transfer the client to other skills.

Parasuicidal behavior of overdosing works in a similar manner. Taking an overdose, if not lethal, almost always either causes headache and vomiting or induces sleep. During sleep we are temporarily not conscious of our negative affect and neurochemicals in our body are readjusted (more specifically serotonin is produced during certain stages of sleep). Most of us feel better after a good nights sleep. So too, the borderline client feels better after sleep induced by overdose.

In addition to these biological responses there may be a variety of environmental reinforcers. Clients may receive attention and support from others following self-injury. Such attention and support may serve as a distractor and/or may directly serve to help them ameliorate their mood. They may be hospitalized where there are distractions, support, and a controlled environment which may remove them from whatever was causing the negative affect. These environmental factors further reinforce the behavior.

A very important distinction must be made here. Too often this dynamic is misinterpreted to mean "She's doing it for attention" and the response is to "ignore" the client to avoid reinforcing the behavior. While in a few cases a client may truly be attention seeking, it is my experience that in most cases the attention is a means to an end. What the client is really seeking is relief from uncomfortable emotions including anxiety or loneliness. Ignoring the client in this case may only escalate their anxiety and discomfort. Thus, it is critical to attend to the negative affect prior to the self injury and provide skills for affective relief. DBT skills that can be used for affective relief are discussed further in Chapter 7.

Finally, as Linehan (1993) states "Suicide is the ultimate in emotion regulation because most all of us think we'll feel better if we're dead." She irreverently points out that the only problem with it is its side effects! This illustrates how clients view suicide as a solution to their emotion dysregulation. They believe if they are dead, things will be better.

I often point out to them that the problem with this solution is that they won't be around to enjoy it if it works! I also point out that we don't know if it works because we don't know with certainty what happens when we die. I ask detailed questions about what they think will happen when they die and I remind them of alternative views. Since we don't know with certainty what happens and since this is a permanent solution which eliminates all other alternatives I suggest that it is best to try absolutely every other possible solution first. In cases where the client has a sense of responsibility or loyalty to others, I will also provide them with a summary of the research that indicates the impact of suicide on others, demonstrating that things will not be better. In other words, I use dialectic persuasion as discussed in Chapter 7 to create cognitive dissonance with the idea that it will make things better or is the only solution.

If the client is using self injury as a means of regulating emotions they must be taught other ways of regulating or tolerating their emotions. Such skills are described in Linehan's (1993) Skills Training Manual as "Emotion Regulation Skills" and "Distress Tolerance Skills" and are summarized in Chapter 7 of this text. Suggesting a less damaging way to elicit a physical response may also useful for these clients. Possible suggestions include splashing ice cold water on themselves, taking a cold (or hot) shower, holding onto ice cubes for 10 minutes, or putting their hands in a bucket of ice water. I will even accept less lethal forms of self injury as long as the overall movement is toward decreasing self injury (ie: burning instead of cutting, cutting on a less lethal place). I have found that any alteration in their rituals (e.g. sterilizing razor blades first) can begin to break the pairing, make the acts less impulsive and more conscious, and begin moving the client out of a "stuck" pattern.

For this reason substitute behaviors with similar visual or motor cues may also be helpful. For example, a client may mark herself with red lipstick or markers instead of cutting. Other activities that cause a physiological response may include exercise such as walking or punching a bag, taking a hot shower or bath, or using a prescribed antianxiety medication. Masturbation to orgasm can also cause a surge of endorphins but this has to be approached carefully especially for those who have been abused or who tend to put themselves in risky sexual situations. It is important not to pair sexual behavior with self injurious behavior and thus, this intervention must be considered and presented carefully.

A list of "alternatives" to self injury is provided in Appendix A. It is always best if the client can generate potential substitute behaviors as this leads to therapeutic ownership and makes compliance more likely.

PARASUICIDAL BEHAVIOR AS A MEANS OF COMMUNICATION

Parasuicidal behavior may also serve as a mean of communication. It may be a means of showing others the emotional pain the client is experiencing—*"I couldn't tell them how upset I was so I decided to show them."* It may also be a means of communicating the significance of their requests or needs—*"No one takes me seriously unless I'm in the hospital."* or *"No one was listening so I decided to show them."* This pattern of communication may be learned in their invalidating environments where their communication of emotions and needs is ignored or punished until it escalates and then is rewarded.

Again this pattern is often negatively labeled as "attention seeking" or "manipulative." In fact, the client lacks the emotion regulation and communication skills to express their needs more directly. Thus, the intervention is to teach them more direct communication skills (i.e. Interpersonal Effectiveness Skills) and what to do if they communicate their needs but their needs go unmet. It is important to validate their needs and communicate that you understand them with an explanation of how you will meet them or why you can't meet them and what they might try instead. Again, simply ignoring the behavior becomes part of the invalidating pattern and usually only leads to further escalation of their communication.

PARASUICIDAL BEHAVIOR AS A MEANS OF RELIEVING DISSOCIATION

The relationship between self injury and dissociation is a very interesting one. Often you will hear clients talk about their parasuicidal behavior in a way that indicates the self-injury provides them with relief from dissociation. *"It brings me back." "It's the only way I feel real."* Research findings indicate that clients tend to experience an escalation of dissociative symptoms (depersonalization, derealization) prior to the self injury, a peak of these symptoms during the injury, with immediate and sustained relief of these symptoms following self-injury (Kemperman, Russ, & Shearin, 1997). Clients who report feeling no pain during self injury report significantly higher rates of dissociative symptoms on the Dissociative Experiences Scale (Kemperman, Russ, & Shearin, 1997). Thus, it is particularly important that clients who deny pain during self injury be evaluated for dissociative disorders as well.

When clients are describing significant levels of dissociation and relief from dissociation via self injury interventions should target the development of other skills to address the dissociative symptoms. The simplest and most obvious of these is reality orientation skills such as teaching the client to be aware of the room in detail, observant of physical sensations that ground them (e.g. *"Be aware of the chair beneath you."*) and using grounding cognitions (e.g. *"Today is Tuesday. I am sitting in my office typing on my computer."*) In part, it may be the strong physical sensation of pain that reorients the client. Again, suggestion of a less damaging alternative may be useful for these clients such as splashing ice cold water on themselves, taking a cold (or hot) shower, holding onto ice cubes for 10 minutes, or putting their hands in a bucket of ice water. Use of a safe support person who can maintain eye contact and provide reassurance may also be useful.

PARASUICIDAL BEHAVIOR AS A MEANS OF STOPPING RACING OR OBSESSIVE THOUGHTS

Sometimes clients will describe parasuicidal behavior as a means of stopping racing thoughts or obsessive thoughts. At times these thoughts will be directly related to self injury (e.g. *"All I could think about was cutting myself. The thoughts just got worse and worse. It was the only way to stop thinking about it."*) but they may also be unrelated (e.g. *"I had so many thoughts running through my head and I couldn't concentrate. Burning myself made them stop. Afterward, my mind was quiet."*) In these situations the rituals around self injury likely serve to refocus attention, the pain may serve as an abrupt and severe distraction which refocuses the mind, and the injury may cause biochemical changes that slow the thought process. When the function of the injury is to stop racing or obsessive thoughts interventions should be aimed at doing the same. Mindfulness techniques, relaxation and refocusing exercises, and thought stopping techniques such as snapping a rubber band on the wrist, can all be useful in this regard.

PARASUICIDAL BEHAVIOR AS A MEANS OF GAINING CONTROL

Clients sometimes describe self-injury as a means of gaining control. *"No one can say what I do to my body but me."* or *"I just felt like everything was out of control and that's the one thing I have control over."* Commonly they will describe it as a means of gaining control over their pain and suffering *"I couldn't control what happened to me but I can control this."* or *"It just hurt so bad. At least then I could see the pain."*

When a client injures to obtain a sense of control it is very important that self-injury not be "taken away" from them but rather approached as something they "give up" because they no longer need it to be in control. Teaching clients ways to be more effective and thus, more in control are critical. It can also be helpful to teach them how to tolerate situations when we don't have control. Thus, their autonomy must always be emphasized. (i.e. *"If this is really what you want to do I know I can't stop you, but you've told me things that suggest you'd like to do something different."* Or *"But I know you don't like the consequences such as . . . so how about if we do something different that you're in control of?"*)

While I have found these five functions of parasuicidal behavior to be most common, there certainly may be other functions as well. Parasuicidal behavior may serve any or all of these functions at various points in the client's life but I have found that for most clients parasuicidal behavior tends to have one or two primary functions. If one can identify which of these functions the behavior serves one then has a strong clue as to where to start in terms of interventions. Again, clients are not likely to give up the parasuicidal behaviors unless they develop other skills and options for addressing those functions.

ASSESSMENT OF PARASUICIDAL BEHAVIOR

In order to determine what function the behavior serves as well as appropriate responses one must do an adequate assessment of the behavior. Further, this assessment must be done to determine the level of risk the behavior presents to the client and the resulting appropriate level of intervention. The obvious purpose of such a risk assessment is to prevent an intentional or unintentional suicide. An additional goal is to avoid reinforcing the behavior and to identify the most helpful but least invasive intervention.

Unfortunately our ability to predict suicide is much poorer than we would like. While there are many psychological assessment tools aimed at identifying suicide risk, none of them have particularly strong predictive validity. (Obviously this is an area where we would want 100% predictive validity!) Thus, the risk assessment generally consists of a detailed interview and review of history in which the assessor tries to obtain as much information as possible about the client's risk factors as well as nature and history of the parasuicidal thoughts and behaviors. The assessor must then weigh both the risk factors and protective factors to determine an appropriate level of response.

SUICIDE RISK FACTORS

In that regard it can be beneficial to be knowledgeable about the behavioral risk factors for suicide which are summarized in Table 4. There are also a number of demographic risk factors for suicide which are summarized elsewhere in the literature.

Table 4: Suicide Risk Factors in the General Population

Factors Predicting Suicide in the General Population

1. Previous lethal attempts
2. Specific plan
3. High intent & high availability of means
4. High impulsivity
5. High substance use
6. Low social support

Further, one should be aware of factors associated with completed suicides in individuals with BPD. Several studies have indicated that Borderlines with prominent depressive symptoms are more likely to complete suicide and depression is clearly a general risk factor for suicide (Dean, 2001; Paris, 1990). In one study, clients with BPD who completed suicide had a mean age of 32. The mean time for suicide was four years after inpatient hospitalization (Paris, 1990). Those who successfully completed suicide often had made prior attempts, were more highly educated than survivors, had fewer psychotic symptoms than survivors as well as fewer problems with their mothers and fewer early separation and losses (Paris, 1990). These findings seem somewhat counter-intuitive. If these findings are accurate, it may be that those clients who were better educated, less psychotic, and had fewer losses either were better able to develop and carry out a lethal plan and/or their difficulties were more incongruent with their environment and abilities and thus, more distressing to them. Nonetheless, these statistics serve as a reminder that those clients who have struggled with this illness for an extended period of time and who can sometimes appear better functioning may actually be even more at risk for completing suicide.

ASSESSMENT OF RISK FACTORS

A description of risk factors as well as sample assessment questions is provided in Tables 5 and 6. Appendix B provides a risk assessment worksheet designed by the author based on a review of other suicide risk assessment tools. The risk assessment worksheet may be reproduced for use with clients. However, it should be noted that this tool has not been empirically validated. It is intended simply as a guideline for assessing and documenting both the risk and protective factors for any given client.

Table 7 provides sample assessment questions and a description of protective factors. Clinicians often are better at assessing and documenting risk factors than protective factors but it is the protective factors that often do, and should, aid in determining the level of intervention as well. Protective factors are those internal and external factors which may protect the client against self injury or suicide.

Table 5: Assessment of Risk Factors: Suicidal Ideation, Plan, and Intent

Risk Factors	Description and/or Examples	Sample Interview Questions
Frequency/ Intensity of Thoughts of Death	Does the client think or dream about dying? How often? How strongly? *"It wouldn't bother me if I died." "Sometimes I wish I could go to sleep and never wake up."*	"Do you ever think about dying? Do you sometimes wish you could go to sleep and not wake up? Does it bother you to think about dying?"
Frequency/ Intensity of Ideation	What thoughts does the client have about suicide? How often? How Intense? *"I think about cutting myself all the time." "I sometimes have a fleeting thought about suicide." "I think about it all day."*	"When is the last time you thought about harming yourself?" "About how often does this happen?"
Plan	Does the client have a specific plan for harming themselves? *"I often think about it but I don't know what I'd do."* vs. *"I think about shooting myself."*	"When you think about hurting yourself, how do you think about doing it?"

Table 5: Assessment of Risk Factors: Suicidal Ideation, Plan, and Intent (Continued)

Risk Factors	Description and/or Examples	Sample Interview Questions
Means	How would the patient harm themselves? What is the lethality of that method? Do they have access to the means? (See Table 8 for ways to assess the risk of the means.)	"Do you have a gun?" "Do you have the pills?" etc. If yes, discuss getting rid of means. If no, "How would you get . . . ?"
Time/Place	Have they identified a specific time and place to execute their plan or do they state a specific circumstance? *"If my wife leaves me I'll do it." "If I don't get my job I know I'll cut myself."*	"When would you do this?" "Do you have a plan for when you'd do this?"
Intended Victim	If at risk for aggression do they identify who they would harm? *"Someday I'm gonna kill someone." vs. "Someday I'm gonna kill my wife's new boyfriend."*	"Who are you planning to harm?" "Is there someone specific you want to get back at?"
Intent	Does the client intend to act on their feelings. *"I think about it but I'd never do it."* vs. *"I'm going to do this and no one can stop me."* Is that intent ego syntonic (comfortable)—*"It's my right to kill myself."* Or dystonic (uncomfortable)—*"I know it's wrong but . . ."*	"On a scale of 1 to 10 how likely are you to act on your feelings?" "If you made a promise not to act on this, how confident are you that you could keep that promise?"

Table 6: Assessment of Risk Factors: Demographic and Behavioral Factors

Risk Factors	Description and/or Examples	Sample Interview Questions
Prior Attempts	Clients with prior attempts are at greater risk. Gather as much data as possible about prior attempts: When? How? How lethal? What happened? Were they discovered? How long before they sought assistance? Did they get treatment?	"Have you tried to hurt yourself before? If so, how? When? How many times? What happened? Did you seek treatment?"
Prior Hospitalizations	Some research has suggest that clients may be at greatest risk within 3 months of inpatient discharge and within 1 year of inpatient discharge. How many times have they been hospitalized? When? For What?	"Have you ever been hospitalized because of trying to hurt yourself or for other mental health reasons?" "When?" "Where?" "What got you into the hospital that time?"
Family/Social History	Any family or social issues which would place the client at risk should be identified especially any family history of suicide, abuse, or lack of familial support?	"Has anyone else in your family committed suicide (or hurt themselves or hurt others)?" General social history questions.
Behavioral Indicators	Any behaviors that may suggest the client is at risk should be identified such as giving things away, making a will, writing a goodbye letter. Include also increased isolation or any sudden changes in behavior such as a client who has been distraught suddenly seeming at peace. For self injury it may include hoarding items. Also, note if client has a tendency to act impulsively.	"Have you made any preparations for hurting yourself?" "Have you thought about what you would do in preparation for your death?" "Have you been saving up medicines? Have you hidden things to hurt yourself with?"

Table 6: Assessment of Risk Factors: Demographic and Behavioral Factors (Continued)

Risk Factors	Description and/or Examples	Sample Interview Questions
Altered Mental State	This includes any alterations in psychological functioning which may place the client at higher risk such as increased agitation or command hallucinations.	"Do you ever hear voices telling you to hurt yourself or someone else?"
Alcohol/Drug Use	Clients who are actively using are at greater risk for becoming distraught and/or impulsive. Clients who are chemically dependent are also at greater risk.	"How much alcohol (or other drugs) do you use?" "How often?" Other questions typical of a general chemical dependency screen.
Other Risk Factors	Any other factors which may place the client at risk should be identified such as demographic risk factors like "elderly male," "homosexual teen" "professional risk" (e.g. psychiatrists, dentists, police officers)	Anything identified in the generally history taking.

Table 7: Assessment of Protective Factors

Risk Factors	Description and/or Examples	Sample Interview Questions
Support System	Does the client have an adequate support system? Is that support system able to monitor and intervene for the client?	"Who do you have for support?" "Is there anyone who can stay with you constantly until these feelings pass?"
Protective Beliefs	This includes any beliefs the client may have that would prevent them from harming themselves. *"It's wrong." "I don't want to go to hell." "I know I'll feel better eventually."*	"What would keep you from harming yourself?" "This probably sounds like a strange question but, why not kill yourself?"

Table 7: Assessment of Protective Factors (Continued)

Risk Factors	**Description and/or Examples**	**Sample Interview Questions**
Fears/ Responsibility	This includes any fears or feelings of responsibility that keep the client from acting on their feelings. *"I'm scared of pain." "I never cut on myself when the kids are around." "I wouldn't do that to my husband." "There'd be no one to take care of my dog."*	"If you did act on these feelings who would it affect?" "How do you think this would effect your family . . .?"
Strong Alliance	Sometimes a client has a strong alliance with another individual to whom they have made a promise not to harm themselves. While this alone cannot be trusted to prevent them from acting in some cases it can be a helpful factor. *"I promised . . . I wouldn't do it."*	"Who would your death most affect?" "Is there anyone you've promised not to hurt yourself?"
History of Resource Use	In the past has the client sought assistance when feeling this way? Do they immediately seek medical attention after self-injury or do they keep it secret?	"In the past when you've had these feelings what have you done?" "In the past when you've injured yourself what happened next?"
Other	Any other things that may reduce the client's risk should be identified.	

Because there is no "formula" or one factor that accurately predicts suicide risk one must consider the risk factors and weigh them against the protective factors in deciding on an appropriate intervention. While at times calculated risks may be taken one should always err on the side of caution. It is better to hospitalize a client that would not have ultimately committed suicide than to not hospitalize a client who ultimately would.

ASSESSING LETHALITY

In assessing potential risk one must consider the means of self injury the client plans to pursue along with the probability the client will be rescued. Table 8 describes the various levels of risk with some sample behavior. Identifying the risk of lethality can be helpful in determining an appropriate level of intervention. For example, two clients who have a plan to cut their wrists may require very different interventions. In many cases, a client who makes superficial cuts on their wrists without suicide intent who lives with someone who is willing to monitor them for safety may remain at home. However, a client who makes deep cuts, has suicidal intent, and lives alone without support may need to be placed on a crisis bed or inpatient facility.

It should be noted that one of the possible interventions is to find a way to increase the probability of rescue. This is especially true when a client remains suicidal while on a locked inpatient, forensic, or correctional unit. In this case the client may be put on observational status. It should be noted however that observations should be made at random with a specified maximum interval. For example, "15 minute checks" means checking the client no less than every 15 minutes. However, the amount of time that passes should not be exactly 15 minutes but should vary. If you check the client at 1:00, 1:15, 1:30, and 1:45 the client will note your pattern, wait for you to come by at 2:00 and implement their plan just after you leave having exactly 14 minutes to complete it.

Table 8: Assessing Lethality

Assessing Risk and Lethality
(from greatest risk to least risk)

Level of Risk	*and*	*Probability of Rescue*
High Risk	&	Low Probability of Rescue (e.g. gunshot with no family around)
High Risk	&	High Probability of Rescue (e.g. lethal overdoes while in hospital)
Low Risk	&	Low Probability of Rescue (e.g. cigarette burns with no one around)
Low Risk	&	High Probability of Rescue (e.g. banging head on wall in jail)

NO HARM CONTRACTS

Unfortunately, too many professionals are taught that the way to complete a suicide risk assessment is to do a no-harm contract. Invariably when I ask workshop participants how to best predict suicide one participant will respond "ask them" and another participant will share a story of how someone with whom they had a contract left their facility and committed suicide.

Let me be very clear. To date there is absolutely *no* evidence that completing a suicide contract will prevent suicide. Further, standards of care do *not* support the completion of a suicide contract as an adequate assessment tool.

Having said that, asking a client to commit to a no harm contract certainly is *one* of the things you may do as part of your assessment. Personally, I use the no self harm contract as an assessment tool and intervention. If a client cannot contract, it is clear we need a strong plan for safety likely including an inpatient hospitalization. If they can't contract indefinitely, I ask them if they can contract not to harm themselves before the next appointment, for the next day, etc. If the client is willing to contract, and I have enough history with the client to know they have strong values against lying, I am more confident of their ability to stay safe. I consider this in light of other risk factors such as their level of impulsivity. If I know the client is "treatment wise" and knows "the right thing to say" I put no stock in their promise but instead consider the other risk factors. If the client says they won't harm themselves but you have reason to think otherwise, document the reasons why you don't think their report is unreliable, and pursue hospitalization.

I had the unfortunate experience of having the mental health director of one of the clinics I worked for commit suicide. Many of his close associates were concerned about him and in hind sight many saw things that they later realized were warning signs. But when asked directly, he had promised his friends not to harm himself. As a mental health professional, he knew exactly what to say and what not to say. Shortly after his friends left his home that day he went to his front yard and shot himself. You can only imagine the effect this had on those who cared about him and to whom he made that promise. *Don't rely on a contract as your only assessment tool!*

In addition, the contract may serve as one of your interventions. Again, for a client who has a strong sense of personal responsibility a contract can increase their level of commitment to staying safe. Having them articulate this promise aloud or in writing can bolster their commitment to keep themselves safe. If they are reluctant to contract one can ask "what would give you more confidence in your ability to stay safe?" Often the answer to this question is therapeutic information that can lead to appropriate interventions.

CHRONIC VERSUS ACUTE RISK

The other problem with most training in risk assessment is that it tends to focus on clients who are at *acute* risk. However many clients, especially those with BPD, struggle with *chronic* risk of self harm. Because some of the interventions that one would use in dealing with someone in acute risk may actually reinforce self destructive patterns it is important to know the difference between acute and chronic risk of harm and how interventions may differ. It should be noted that *patients can be in a state of both chronic and acute suicidality.* Fine (1990) provides an excellent overview of the differences between chronic and acute suicide risk and appropriate features of each which are summarized briefly here.

When a client is in acute risk for suicide or accidental death, patient autonomy and confidentiality are overridden temporarily in an effort to preserve life. Professional standards of care are clear for acute suicidality. Interventions for acute suicidality include immediate and active assessment of risk and the determination of appropriate treatment setting.

When clients are chronically parasuicidal, the risk of suicide or accidental death is chronic but not imminent. Suicidality is a chronic state for these individuals in which the parasuicidal behavior is a mode of adaptation to life. Danger of death exists but is less clear or potentially lethal. In these cases, hospitalization may not be helpful and in fact, may be harmful, as it may reinforce maladaptive behavioral patterns or remove clients from the very situations that he or she needs to learn to deal with.

When there is chronic parasuicidal risk the therapist must reinforce the client's personal responsibility for his or her behavior. The therapist explores with the client the interpersonal dynamics of the behavior. At times some risk to life is assumed in order to preserve the autonomy of the patient.

Standards of care for dealing with a chronically suicidal patient are much less clear. However, Fine (1990) recommends the following interventions: 1) exploring the interpersonal function of the behavior; 2) emphasizing that the patient is ultimately responsible for his or her own welfare; 3) resisting the temptation to make extraordinary treatment arrangements; 4) setting and enforcing clear and explicit limits regarding how much suicidal behavior will be tolerated; 5) initiating involuntary hospitalization only when chronic threats cross over into an acute suicidal state; 6) with the patient's consent, informing family members that suicide risk is chronic and of realistic therapeutic expectations; 7) carefully documenting the therapeutic procedures followed emphasizing the determination of a chronic (rather than acute) suicidal situation and rationale for interventions.

Suggestions for dealing with common problems in crisis intervention and parasuicide risk are provided in Chapter 7. Linehan (1993) also provides suggestions for reducing chronic parasuicidal behavior. She suggests approaching chronic parasuicidal behavior as a therapy interfering behavior which is addressed through the process of behavioral analysis. A behavioral chain analysis is an in depth analysis of an instance or set of instances of a problem or targeted behavior in which the therapist and client attempt to determine the factors leading up to, following, and "controlling" reinforcing or influencing the behavior. It is through this detailed and ongoing investigation that changes in the behavior can be made.

Thus, Linehan (1993, 1995) suggests the following strategies for decreasing suicidal behaviors. First, as already discussed a thorough assessment should be done including the frequency, intensity, and severity of the behavior. Second, a behavioral chain analysis is conducted in which factors influencing behavior are determine and positive changes are reinforced. Third, the therapist discusses with the client alternative solutions to problems as well as learning to tolerate distress. Fourth, the negative effects of suicidal behavior are emphasized. Fifth, a non-suicidal plan is developed and strategies are used to help the client commit to this plan. Sixth, the therapist must validate the patient's emotional pain. Again, validating the client's emotional ex, a behavioral chain analysis is conducted in which factors influencing behavior are determine and positive changes are reinforced. Third, the therapist discusses with the client alternative solutions to problems as well as learning to tolerate distress. Fourth, the negative effects of suicidal behavior are emphasized. Fifth, a non-suicidal plan is developed and strategies are used to help the client commit to this plan. Sixth, the therapist must validate the patient's emotional pain. Again, balancing validation of the client's emotional experience with change strategies is critical in the execution of DBT. Lastly, the therapist attempts to connect the client's current behavior to overall patterns.

In the behavioral chain analysis the problem must be clearly defined in terms of behavior. Next a step by step description of the chain of events leading up to and following the behavior is developed. This includes the clients emotions, bodily sensations, thoughts and images, overt behaviors, and environmental factors in as much detail as possible. This involves first identifying when the behavioral chain began or pinpointing as much as possible the precipitating event. Then the "behavioral links" are explored by breaking the behavior into very small units. This is done by asking questions such as "What next?" or "How did you get from ___ to ___?" Finally an evaluation of consequences of the behavior which either reinforce or weaken problematic behaviors is conducted.

It is important in this process that the therapist not "assume" what the antecedents and consequences of behavior are but rather take an attitude of curiosity and naiveté. In this way the therapist gains information from the client about what specific functions and reinforcers exist for that individual. Once these are identified, appropriate alternatives can be explored.

DOCUMENTATION OF RISK ASSESSMENT

Not only does one have to conduct a risk assessment but one must document that you have done so. For legal purposes, if it's not documented, it didn't happen. Table 9 summarizes the components of adequate documentation and Table 10 provides a sample progress note.

Table 9: Documentation of Risk Evaluation & Intervention

To ensure care and reduce risk always . . .

- document review of prior records.
- document assessment of risk.
- document inhibiting or protective factors.
- document actions considered.
- document why you decided to take the actions you took or why you chose not to act.
- document names & dates of consultants.
- inform your clinical supervisor and document that you have done so.
- document all related phone calls.
- document patient's reactions to the interventions.

Table 10: Sample Progress Note

08/08/2002 T.C. from client stating that she feels like cutting on her arm because she is angry with her mother for not sending her a birthday card. Denies intent to kill herself stating, "I'm just so mad. She doesn't care about me. I wish I was never born." States she has razor blades in her bathroom but agrees to give them to her roommate. I speak with roommate and confirm she will lock up blades and observe client. Client denies access to other means but states "I can always get some more." Agrees to call back if she is considering going to the store. Records indicate a history of cutting on herself in the past but always superficially and she consistently seeks treatment following self injurious behavior thus she does not appear at imminent lethal risk. Agrees to take a walk and talk to her roommate about how frustrated she is. Agrees to call on-call services if intent returns. She talks at length regarding her feelings of abandonment by her mother and states by the end of our call "I feel better." in a calm tone. T.C. to on-call worker advising her of the situation. Message left for clinical supervisor.

Colleen E. Warner, Psy.D., LP

CHAPTER SUMMARY

Dealing with parasuicidal behavior is most certainly one of the most difficult aspects of dealing with clients with BPD. About 80 percent of Borderlines engage in parasuicidal behavior while approximately 10 percent complete suicide. The clinician must be well versed in the assessment and documentation of both the risk factors and protective factors related to self injury. In determining the level of intervention needed one should assess the potential lethality of the method as well as the probability of rescue. Both removal of means and interventions aimed at increasing probability of rescue are appropriate, although not necessarily sufficient, interventions.

In intervening with parasuicidal behavior it is critical that the clinician also assess the function of the behavior. Parasuicidal behavior often has one of five functions: 1) Emotion Regulation; 2) Communication; 3)Relief from dissociation; 4) Relief from racing or obsessive thoughts; and 5) Maintaining a sense of control (especially control of pain or of their bodies). By identifying the functions the behavior serves, the clinician can then focus on interventions to address these problems. Remember, the client with BPD views parasuicidal behavior as a solution not a problem. Thus, the skilled clinician will help the client learn alternative solutions so that she becomes willing and able to give up the parasuicidal behavior.

6

Succeeding: Effective Treatment for Borderline Personality Disorder

RECOVERY RATES & PROGNOSTIC INDICATORS

In spite of the historical professional lore that clients with BPD are "untreatable" research consistently indicates that the vast majority of clients with BPD improve and many improve to the point that they no longer meet diagnostic criteria. Even more interesting is that they seem to improve at relatively consistent rates across studies although the time intervals for reassessment may vary by study. Studies generally indicate that between 30 to 49 percent of Borderlines no longer meet diagnostic criteria somewhere between two and four years after hospitalization (Dean, 2001; Zanarini, 2003). Approximately 75 percent no longer meet diagnostic criteria at follow up between 6 and 15 years (Dean, 2001; Zanarini, 2003). Most clients with BPD no longer meet full criteria for the disorder by age 40 and even more show improvement by age 50 (Paris, 2002).

A legitimate question is whether or not this improvement occurs with or without treatment. That question may never be adequately addressed for ethical reasons. Given the severity of BPD and the potential for self-harm and even death it would be unethical to engage in a study including a no treatment control group. As a result, the vast majority of this research is conducted as follow up to inpatient hospitalizations where there is no control group and no control over whether or not clients participated in treatment or for kind of treatment. However, as will be discussed later in this chapter Dialectic Behavioral Therapy has been found to produce more rapid and significant results than other forms of therapy.

Another legitimate question is to what degree these clients may relapse. In that regard Zanarini (2003) found only 5.9% of those clients experiencing remissions later experienced recurrences. Impulsive symptoms tend to resolve most quickly. Affective symptoms, especially dysphoria, are most chronic. Cognitive and interpersonal symptoms tend to vary over time (Dean, 2001; Zanarini, 2003). Clients with more severe symptoms, who abuse chemicals, who have prominent antisocial traits, and who experience significant dysphoria tend to have a poorer prognosis (Dean, 2001; Plakun, 1991).

Thus, there is strong indication that these clients do improve but that it tends to take a long time. The short term prognosis tends to be poor with impulsive behavior and high rates of treatment drop out. For this reason it is advisable to view BPD more as a chronic disorder which must be "managed" rather than cured. This alleviates the pressure on both the client and clinician to provide a "magic cure" and reduces the anxiety and shame associated with temporary set backs.

For this reason, when I accept a client with BPD I make the assumption that it is "for life." In other words, unless I die, the client dies, one of us moves, or fiscal issues prohibit our relationship (in other words I do expect to get paid) I agree to be her therapist. Clients can (and often do) "fire" me or drop out of treatment but I view this as part of the BPD behavior and allow them to renegotiate to restart therapy within certain parameters. I do not "fire" clients with BPD for noncompliance (although I do "fire" other patients for this reason) because again, I view this as a symptom of their disorder. That is not to say we may not take a "therapeutic vacation" but again, the parameters for restarting therapy are fully explained.

That is not to say that I would never discontinue therapy with a client with BPD. Certainly if there became unresolvable countertransference issues, a conflict of interest, or a direct threat to myself of my family we would discontinue services and a therapeutic transfer would be arranged. This intervention must be done very thoughtfully and for clinically sound reasons and not just as an acting out of the clinician's frustration and anger. Generally this may be appropriate only when one is attempting to create a behavior change by removing a reinforcer or creating an adverse consequence. Great care must be given to assure that this is clinically indicated and done in a caring, respectful manner. Again, care should be taken that clinician is not just "giving up" or punishing the client. For this reason, consultation and supervision are vital for even the most seasoned clinician whenever such action is being considered.

In most cases, these "noncompliance" issues are explained by the very disorder that brings about their need for therapy in the first place. Thus, such behaviors are approached and processed as therapy interfering behaviors which are addressed as part of the DBT process.

While I do not always articulate this position to clients I believe it is extremely important in the therapeutic process. Such a position allows me to view situations with a long term perspective and thus be less anxious and reactive and more therapeutic. Further, I believe this commitment is communicated to clients nonverbally by my affect and actions and serves to alleviate some of their abandonment anxiety.

PSYCHOPHARMACOLOGICAL APPROACHES

Experts agree that psychopharmacotherapy alone is insufficient to treat BPD. It must be combined with psychosocial treatment. To date there are no studies comparing psychotherapy to medication treatment and given ethical considerations such research is unlikely. Clinical wisdom is that both are necessary components to treatment.

While no one medication has been found to be superior in treating BPD, pharmacological agents may be most useful in treating acute symptoms of clusters of: 1) affective instability; 2) impulsive/aggressive behavior; and 3) transient psychosis or dissociation. Algorithms for psychopharmacological treatment according to symptom cluster have been developed by Soloff (1994; 2000) and are consistent with the recommendations of the American Psychiatric Association (2001). These are summarized in Table 11.

Table 11: Algorithms for Psychopharmacological Treatment of BPD (Soloff, 2000)

For Affective Symptoms:	For Impulsive Symptoms:	For Psychotic Symptoms:
1) Start with SSRI (if rapid response is needed, a low-dose conventional neuroleptic). 2) If response to SSRI is inadequate, ADD/SWITCH to a low dose neuroleptic. 3) If response is still poor, ADD/SWITCH to lithium or MAOI. 4) SWITCH to carbamazepine or valproate, if no response. 5) If necessary, ADD atypical neuroleptic.	1) Start with SSRI or related antidepressant 2) If response is inadequate, SWITCH to a different SSRI or related antidepressant. 3) If response is still poor, AUGMENT with a benzodiazepine or a low-dose neuroleptic. 4) If response remains inadequate SWITCH to MAOI. 5) Finally, add/switch to lithium or a mood stabilizer.	1) START with a low-dose typical neuroleptic 2) If poor/partial response, INCREASE dose. 3) If response still poor, RECONSIDER DIAGNOSIS. If symptoms are mood congruent, treat for affective symptoms. 4) If symptoms do NOT have a major mood component, SWITCH to clozapine or another atypical antipsychotic.

The advantage of using medication is that it may increase cognitive and affective functioning to the degree that the client may be better able to engage in and benefit from psychotherapy. Unfortunately, some clients may perceive the suggestion of medication as an insult or negative indication of their condition. Other client's may have a tendency to look for a "magic pill" rather then focus on making therapeutic changes.

Further, the prescribing physician must balance the potential benefits of any medication with the potential risks of that medication as well as accessibility and cost factors. Because clients with BPD have such a high risk of overdosing the physician may stay away from a medication which, while likely beneficial, has a high risk of lethality. Instead the physician is likely to chose a much less lethal medication that will likely be beneficial. Again this one of the benefits of the SSRI medications in that they tend to have fewer side effects and are much less likely to be lethal.

Medication compliance is often an issue with clients with BPD. Clients will often refuse medications, take them inconsistently, or stop them abruptly. Clients may have a tendency to overattribute symptoms as a side effects of the medication leading to further noncompliance. In addition, they may engage in "creative compliance" where they take the medication but not precisely as prescribed.

OTHER BIOLOGICAL TREATMENTS

As some clients are resistant to the notion of any medication intervention but may be willing to consider "herbal" or "natural remedies" it is worth mentioning that at least one study reports some success in the use of Omega-3 fatty acid treatment for women with BPD. In a double-blind, placebo-controlled pilot study Zanarini and Frankenburg (2003) found treatment with ethyl-eicosapentaenoic acid (E.EPA) to be superior to placebo in reducing aggression and the severity of depressive symptoms in women with BPD. The usual cautions about naturalistic remedies as opposed to medication apply. However, this may be an alternative worth exploring for clients who refuse psychotropics.

PSYCHOTHERAPEUTIC APPROACHES

Two psychotherapeutic approaches have been found to be efficacious in randomized controlled trials with clients with BPD: Psychoanalytic/Psychodynamic approaches and Dialectic Behavioral Therapy (APA, 2001). It should be noted that in both cases the controlled trials involved structured therapeutic programs rather than just individual psychotherapy. Both approaches involved three components: 1) weekly individual psychotherapy; 2) one or more weekly group sessions; and 3) meetings between therapists for consultation and supervision. To date the efficacy of these two approaches has not been compared in clinical trials but such research is on the horizon. Because of the relatively larger body of research supporting the use of Dialectic Behavioral Therapy (DBT) in working with clients with BPD it is this approach I chose to emphasize in this text.

COMMONALITIES BETWEEN APPROACHES

Other clinical approaches may be useful in the treatment of BPD however to date they lack empirical validation. It is my experience that these approaches generally have much in common but may use a different language to talk about similar concepts. According to

Dean (1999) there are five constants of individual psychotherapy for clients with BPD regardless of theoretical orientation. These include: 1) Creating a stable treatment environment; 2) Providing active interventions and responses; 3) Establishing a Connection Between the client's actions and present feelings; 4) Taking the gratification out of performing self destructive behaviors; and 5) Paying careful attention to countertransference feelings. Similarly, the American Psychiatric Association's Recommendations for Treatment of BPD suggests the following "common features" to guide the therapist regardless of therapeutic orientation: 1) A strong alliance with the patient; 2) Therapists must be active, interactive, and responsive; 3) Therapists must validate the reality of mistreatment and suffering; 4) In addition to validation the therapist must help the client take appropriate responsibility for their actions; and 5) The therapist must promote reflection rather than impulsive action.

SUMMARY OF DBT EFFICACY TREATMENT

In clinical trials, DBT is compared to "Treatment As Usual" (TAU) in the community. In other words, clients in the control group continued to receive whatever form of services they had previously been receiving while the experimental group participated in a structured DBT program. In these clinical trials DBT has consistently been found to: 1) Reduce the number of clients who are engaging in self injury; 2) Decrease the number of times clients engage in parasuicidal behavior; 3) Reduce the Medical Risk of the Parasuicidal Behaviors: 4) Reduce Treatment Drop-Out; 5) Reduce Psychiatric Inpatient Days; 6) Reduce Client Anger. Clients who participated in DBT also demonstrated improved social and global adjustment. A summary of efficacy studies related to Dialectic Behavioral Therapy may be found at www.behavioraltech.com.

Clinical trials have also consistently supported the cost effectiveness of DBT. For example, the Mental Health Center of Greater Manchester, New Hampshire piloted a study in which they provided comprehensive DBT in and outpatient setting. The team received intensive 10-day training in DBT over a 6 month period of time. Pre-Post data was collected for the first 14 patients receiving DBT. The cost of treatment for these clients was reduced by more than half—from $645,000 to $273,000. This was in large part due to a decreased use of hospitalization and emergency services. The program demonstrated a 77% decrease in hospital days, 76% decrease in partial hospital days, 56% decrease in crisis bed use, and an 80% decrease in face-to-face contact with emergency services (APA,1998). It should be noted that at least one study found decreased health service utilization costs for clients treated in a psychoanalytically oriented partial hospitalizing program as well (Bateman & Fonagy, 2003).

CHAPTER SUMMARY

In spite of clinical lore that clients with BPD are "untreatable" research consistently demonstrates that these clients do get better over time. However, this tends to be a more chronic disorder which for most clients requires a minimum of one year of therapy. Impulsive symptoms tend to resolve the most quickly while dysphoria seems to be the most chronic symptoms. Medications may be effective in treating the primary symptom domains in BPD but no one medication is found to be superior, and the recommendation is for a combination of medication and psychotherapy.

All treatment approaches involve stability in the treatment environment, active interventions, a combination or validation and insistence that the client take responsibility for their actions, and careful attention to countertransference issues. Both DBT and psychodynamic psychotherapies have been demonstrated to be superior to treatment as usual in clinical trials. However, in both cases these clinical trials involved rather structured outpatient or partial hospitalization programs. In multiple clinical trials DBT has been found to be a cost-effective alternative which reduces the frequency and severity of parasuicidal behaviors, lessens the need for inpatient interventions, and has lower drop out rates.

7

One Success Story: An Understanding of DBT

Given the relatively large body of efficacy research supporting the use of DBT with clients with BPD this approach is currently thought by many clinicians to be the treatment of choice. This approach is described in detail in the books "Cognitive Behavioral Treatment of Borderline Personality Disorder" and the accompanying "Skills Training Manual for Treating Borderline Personality Disorder" by Marsha Linehan. Dr. Linehan also offers a series of videotapes as well as trainings in DBT through the Behavioral Technology Transfer group (go to www.behavioraltech.com).

While many clinicians have sought specific training in DBT, I am continually amazed at how many clinicians, many of whom are on the "front lines" in treating clients with BPD, have never heard of the approach or have only a very limited knowledge. Those who have attempted to orient themselves to the approach often complain that it is "overwhelming," "too technical," or "doesn't fit my setting" or simply takes too long to learn. Thus, unfortunately, those who may benefit most from this knowledge often find it inaccessible.

DBT is a rich and detailed treatment approach which, like any good therapeutic model, does require intensive study to execute skillfully. However, it has been my experience that the concepts contained in DBT are very understandable and applicable across settings if one breaks the learning down into small segments. Thus, this chapter attempts to provide a history and overview of the approach as an introduction to the novice. In addition, even those skilled in the application of DBT may benefit from a review of some of the key concepts of the approach. Again, the reader is referred to the above references for a more detailed discussion.

HISTORY OF DBT

Dialectic Behavioral Therapy was developed by psychologist, Dr. Marsha Linehan, at the University of Washington in Seattle. Interestingly, it was not Dr. Linehan's original intent to study BPD. Dr. Linehan was a suicidologist interested in understanding and treating persons with chronic suicidal ideation and multiple suicide attempts. It is not surprising that when she asked for subjects with multiple suicide attempts many clients with BPD were referred. Thus, her research eventually became focused on those with BPD.

Dr. Linehan and her student assistants, using one-way mirrors, observed and documented countless therapeutic sessions with these clients in an attempt to define what therapeutic techniques were being used and were effective with these clients. From this work she developed a model of treatment which, as previously noted, as been consistently found in clinical trials to be effective for clients with BPD.

As a therapist primarily trained in Cognitive Behavioral Therapy (CBT), Dr. Linehan initially focused on the application of CBT with these clients. Those well versed in CBT will note that many of the techniques described in the model are traditional cognitive behavioral approaches (e.g. behavior chain analysis, contingency management, shaping, etc.). While traditional CBT approaches may be effective with clients with BPD, Linehan found it very difficult to get them to engage in such approaches alone. CBT strategies tend to be very "change" focused. Unfortunately when you suggest a Borderline client change one of two things tends to happen. Either she becomes very shame based ("See, it's all my fault.") or she becomes angry at the suggestion that the problem is within her ("You don't understand either.") Neither approach serves as a good foundation for therapeutic motivation.

Thus, Linehan found that in addition to traditional CBT approaches, other skills must be applied. She calls these other techniques "acceptance strategies." These techniques include such skills as validation, "radical acceptance," mindfulness, acknowledging the "wise mind," and cheerleading strategies. Coincidentally, at the time Dr. Linehan was studying Zen Buddhism in her personal life and she incorporated many acceptance strategies from this philosophy into the treatment. She found that it was the consistent tension and balance of both these acceptance and change strategies that was most effective with these individuals.

Also at this time she was studying dialectic philosophy. In short, dialectic philosophy is world view which postulates that everything in our reality consists as a tension between polar opposites and that we consistently seek to resolve this tension. For example, the concepts of change and acceptance can be thought of as opposite tensions. In DBT the therapist is constantly trying to work with both ends of this polarity.

Dialectics is also a method of persuasion, and Linehan discusses using dialectic persuasion as part of the therapeutic process. She defines dialectic persuasion as "A method of logic or argument by disclosing the contradictions (antithesis) in an opponent's argument (thesis) and overcoming them (synthesis)." In other words, the therapist attempts to alter the clients thinking by raising questions or contradictions to their point of view using techniques such as entering into the paradox, using metaphor, playing devil's advocate, or extending their position or argument further.

Linehan further argues that Borderline behavior is in part caused by the client's failed ability to resolve dialectics. Dialectics becomes both a way of understanding Borderline behavior (failed resolution of dialectics) and a method of persuasion in eliciting change. Thus to distinguish the model from traditional Cognitive Behavioral models, she named this treatment Dialectic Behavioral Therapy (DBT).

An example which may make this construct more clear to the reader comes from one of the most classic descriptors of Borderline behavior. Borderlines are often described as having "black and white" or "all or nothing" thinking. This is clearly a description of their failure at resolving dialectic ideas. The therapists task is to help the client see that there is not only black and white, but also gray, and sometimes "polka dot." For example, Borderline clients often view individuals as "all good" or "all bad" when in reality any given individual likely has both favorable and unfavorable qualities.

PRINCIPLE VS. PROTOCOL DRIVEN TREATMENTS

In understanding any therapeutic approach it can be helpful to recognize the difference between principle driven treatments and protocol driven treatments. For example, psychodynamic psychotherapy is primarily principle driven. Psychodynamic theory provides basic concepts or principles and techniques but there is great individual differences in how the therapist applies this theory. Still other approaches are principle driven or "manualized" treatments (e.g. the Cannabis Youth Treatment Program recently published by SAMSA) in which there are very specific instructions for what the therapist does both within and between sessions.

DBT is both a principle and protocol driven treatment approach. In other words, there are basic concepts or principles that underlie the treatment and inform the therapist. In addition, there is a protocol for teaching skills to the client contained primarily in the Skills Training Manual. There are also certain protocols for determining the order in which issues are addressed in therapy.

It should be noted that the clinical efficacy studies of DBT involve both the utilization of the principles and the protocol. This is not to say that either may not be useful in and of themselves but that we only know of their efficacy in combination. It is my recommendation that clinicians who are first learning the model or have limited time to learn the model focus initially on the principles of the model.

I suggest beginning with an understanding of the principles for two reasons. First, the principles are applicable across settings. I have seen the understanding of these principles benefit a variety of clinicians, family members and clergy dealing with individuals with BPD. Many of these individuals may not have the time nor resources to apply the full protocol (although I would note that much of the protocol can be adapted to a variety of settings). Second, it is my experience that an understanding of the principles is necessary to the proper application of the protocol. Without an understanding of *why* you are doing what you are doing many techniques will be misapplied and fail.

This is difficult for many clinicians to accept because their response is often "but I want to know what to *do*." If every client situation was the same this might be possible however, human behavior is much more complex. Understanding the principles will help the clinician make better decisions about what to do and when to do it. It is the skilled combination of therapeutic protocols with sound theory and good clinical judgment that is likely to be most effective.

DBT ASSUMPTIONS ABOUT PATIENTS & THERAPY

Having said this, a number of principles of DBT are contained in the assumptions that DBT makes about patients and therapy which are listed in Table 12. I would argue that even a clinician who chooses not to use the DBT model benefits greatly from the adoption of these assumptions because these assumptions are more helpful cognitions to the clinician than the traditional responses such as "she'll never get better."

Table 12: DBT Assumptions about Patients & Therapy (Linehan, 1993)

- Patients are doing the best they can.
- Patients want to improve.
- Patients need to do better, try harder, and/or be more motivated to change.
- Patients may not have caused all of their own problems but they have to solve them anyway.
- The lives of suicidal, borderline individuals are unbearable as they are currently being lived.
- Patients must learn new behaviors in all relevant contexts.
- Patients cannot fail in therapy.
- Therapists treating borderline patients need support.

COMPONENTS OF THE DBT PROGRAM

Having said that DBT consists of both principles and protocols one should have a basic understanding of the treatment modes utilized in the clinical trials of DBT. Again this is not to say that alterations in this design may not be effective only that the research to date incorporated the following treatment modes. Clients participated in the following four modes of treatment concurrently for a minimum of 6 months.

All clients received Outpatient Individual Psychotherapy for a minimum of 50 minutes per week with a DBT trained individual therapist. Occasionally on a time limited basis and for certain clinical reasons individual psychotherapy may occur twice a week or be extended to between 90 and 120 minutes. All clients must participate in individual psychotherapy to be part of the program. The individual psychotherapist is considered the "primary" therapist and all other approaches revolve around the individual therapy.

Clients also must participate in Outpatient Group Skills Training for 2½ hours per week. It is recommended that the skills training facilitator be different than the individual psychotherapist. The Skills Training Group is psychoeducational in nature and is based on the protocol outlined in the Skills Training Manual.

In addition, clients may utilize phone consultation between appointments. In DBT, Telephone Consultation is considered an important component of the treatment. There are three reasons why telephone consultation is important in the treatment of clients with BPD. First, many Borderline clients have maladaptive skills for asking for help and this provides them an opportunity to learn effective strategies for seeking assistance. Second, Borderlines often have difficulty generalizing skills between sessions. Telephone consultation provides an opportunity for them to seek "coaching" in the applications of their new skills between sessions. Finally, following a particularly difficult session or misunderstanding, phone consultation allows the client an opportunity to connect with the therapist before the next session in order to regain a sense of therapeutic alliance and ward off feelings of insecurity or abandonment. Suggestions for handling telephone consultation are provided later in this chapter.

Because treating Borderline clients can be especially stressful therapist participation in Case Consultation Meetings is also considered an important component of DBT. Case consultation meetings are held weekly and may vary in length of time depending on the number of therapists and cases involved. Both the individual and group therapists, as well as any other members of the patients treatment team, should attend the same consultation group. The aim of the consultation group is to address any problems which arise in the therapists' delivery of the treatment. This is especially important in the treatment of clients with BPD because therapists are especially at risk for developing unhelpful behaviors with this difficult population.

Patients participating in the DBT clinical trials may have also received uncontrolled ancillary treatments such as psychopharmacological interventions, inpatient hospitalization, or vocational rehabilitation services. Since it would be unethical to deny patients these interventions if they may be beneficial, the use of such interventions could not be controlled. For example, it would be unethical to deny a patient who self injured hospital treatment simply because she was part of the research group! While there are no specific protocols for the inclusion of these ancillary treatments there is also nothing in the DBT model that would contraindicate them. Since these ancillary treatments were also not controlled in the control group one may safely assume that any effect they may have had would cancel each other out.

THE SKILLS TRAINING MODULES

As previously noted the protocol for skills training is provided in Linehan's Skills Training Manual. While skills training can be conducted in individual sessions it is generally recommended that the skills training be conducted in groups. Groups may be as small as 2 but ideally would be between 6 and 8 clients.

The skills training consists of four modules including: 1) Mindfulness Skills; 2) Emotion Regulation Skills; 3) Interpersonal Effectiveness Skills and 4) Distress Tolerance Skills. In keeping with the dialectic of change and acceptance two of these modules focus on acceptance skills (Mindfulness and Distress Tolerance) while two focus on change skills (Emotion Regulation and Interpersonal Effectiveness).

While there is flexibility in the time frame and order of the skills training modules it is generally recommended that the skills be taught over a 6 month period. Usually Mindfulness Skills are covered in the first two weeks with eight weeks spent on each of the remaining modules. Further training in mindfulness is incorporated into the other modules. In addition, clients can choose to repeat the skills training group as necessary.

In reviewing these skills training modules I find that many of the concepts are similar to skills many therapists may already teach under different names (e.g. "Assertiveness training is an "interpersonal effectiveness" skill). However, what I find impressive is the detailed yet simplistic way Linehan defines and describes such skills. In this way she breaks down abstract skills that many of us just do automatically into understandable step by step instructions for the Borderline client who does not appear to have these capabilities innately. I will briefly summarize these skills here and the reader is referred to the text and skills training manual for a full discussion.

MINDFULNESS SKILLS

Mindfulness skills are based on the Buddhist concept of mindfulness which may be defined as being aware of a situation (emotion, thought) without making judgments about it. In a sense it is teaching the client self observation and awareness skills. As importantly, it is teaching the client to make such observations without passing judgment or trying to change the situation. For example, many clients with BPD have difficulty identifying their feelings. Mindfulness skills involve learning to observe both the physical sensations associated with emotion and label the emotion. (e.g. I notice my jaw clenching and my breathing increasing. That hurt my feelings. I'm feeling angry.) Such skills often involve self observation, relaxation, and/or meditation skills. In short, it is teaching the client to observe, describe, and participate in an experience without judging or changing it.

An important concept in the mindfulness is that of the "Wise Mind." This notion postulates that we have an "emotional mind" which is driven by our feelings and a "reasonable mind" which is driven by what is rational or intellectual reasonable. The "Wise Mind" balances emotions and reason to direct our course of action to our best interest. Wise mind is defined as the "part of each person that can know and experience the truth" (Linehan, 1993). Sometimes people describe it as their "heart of hearts," "inner wisdom" or "center." It is the feeling of what is right that comes from deep within us rather than from our current emotional state.

Too often Borderline clients make decisions based on what they "think" they "should" do or based on their strong emotional state. Neither generally leads to the most productive decisions. Mindfulness skills teach the clients to pay attention to many different ways of knowing in order to make judgments in their best interest. For this reason, the concept of mindfulness permeates throughout the other skills.

EMOTION REGULATION SKILLS

If DBT assumes that BPD is a result of a primary dysfunction in the emotion regulation skills then it follows that the development of skills to regulate emotions would be an important component of the treatment. Emotion Regulation Skills include: 1) Identifying obstacle to changing emotions; 2) Reducing vulnerability to emotions; 3) Increasing positive emotional events; 4) Increasing mindfulness to current emotions; 5) Acting opposite; and 6) Applying distress tolerance techniques (Linehan, 1993). Obviously an important component of this is being mindful of one's emotional state. Often client with BPD have to be taught how to identify and label emotions. They must also learn to identify any obstacles to changing their emotions. In other words it is difficult to change emotional behaviors if such behavior is followed by reinforcing consequences. Thus, these consequences must be identified and addressed if the emotion is to change.

Clients must also learn to reduce their "vulnerability to the emotional mind." The simple fact is that people are more vulnerable to painful emotions when they become physically or environmentally stressed. This skill reminds me of the acronym "HALT" often used by AA members. In this case, HALT stands for "Don't let yourself get hungry, angry, lonely, or tired." It is thought that these conditions make the alcoholic more prone to relapse. Likewise the client who is fatigued, poorly nourished, in physical pain, or on mood altering chemicals is more prone to emotional dysregulation. Environmental stressors like poverty, abuse, noise, heat or cold can also increase one's vulnerability. Thus, clients are encouraged to target any behaviors or environmental conditions that may increase their vulnerability. Clients are encouraged to get adequate sleep and nutrition, limit caffeine and alcohol use, avoid mood altering chemicals, take their medications as prescribed, avoid certain stressful environments, and engage in activities that increase their self confidence.

Clients are encouraged to increase positive emotional events in their lives. Those with training in cognitive behavioral training may think this sounds suspiciously like the "pleasurable events schedule" and they would be accurate in that assessment. One way to increase positive emotions is to increase participation in activities that elicit such emotions. Thus, clients are taught to identify and schedule activities which bring them pleasure.

Lastly, emotion regulation includes something Linehan calls "opposite action." Since behavioral expression of an emotion is an important part of the emotional experience it follows that one might be able to change the emotion by changing it's behavioral manifestation. In other words, if you want to change your emotion do the opposite of what you feel like doing.

Linehan describes how every emotion has a usual action and opposite action. For example, when anxious we tend to avoid situations. Thus, the opposite action would be to approach the situation. It should be emphasized that this is different than suppressing or blocking an emotion. Opposite action should only be used when the client wants to change an emotion. It is a conscious choice to express another emotion rather than just hide the current emotion.

INTERPERSONAL EFFECTIVENESS SKILLS

Interpersonal Effectiveness Skills in DBT are very similar to the assertiveness training and interpersonal problem solving skills with which many clinicians are familiar. Linehan breaks these skills down into skills for asking for what one needs, saying no, and maintaining the relationship. One of the important points of the Interpersonal Effectiveness Module is that one must balance three priorities: obtaining one's goals in a situation and maintaining both the relationship and self respect.

While Borderline clients often have good social skills in some situations, their tendency in relationships is to sacrifice one of these priorities in the service of another. Thus, they may intensely seek a goal while disregarding the effect on the relationship or sacrifice their self respect in an effort to maintain a relationship. Interpersonal Effectiveness Training helps them learn to balance these priorities by providing skills to address each priority and by providing skills for judging how intensely to ask for something or say no to something. This module also encourages clients to build mastery by practicing a number of interpersonal situations, looking at obstacles to effectiveness and providing "cheerleading statements" or cognitions to encourage effective interpersonal behavior.

DISTRESS TOLERANCE SKILLS

The distress tolerance skills module focuses on skills used to tolerate and accept a difficult or painful situation. As previously noted distress tolerance skills are acceptance skills. While many interventions are aimed at helping the client change their life circumstances the reality is that not all painful experiences can be changed. Grief, pain, discomfort, and distress are all parts of life that cannot be completely avoided. Thus, such uncomfortable feelings must at times be tolerated. The goal of distress tolerance skills is to learn to bear pain skillfully. Linehan (1993) defines distress tolerance as "the ability to perceive one's environment without putting demands on it to be different, to experience your current emotional state without attempting to change it, and to observe your own thoughts and action patterns without attempting to stop or control them." Distress tolerance should not be misconstrued to mean that one approves of a situation only that one learns to accept a situation.

For example, when a love one dies we may experience feelings of shock, disbelief, anger, sadness, loss, etc. Nothing we do can change the fact that they have passed. We do not "approve" of the situation but rather would prefer it never happened. Nonetheless, we must accept the reality of the situation and our feelings about it. Those unable or unwilling to experience these feelings of grief may end up developing complicated grief reactions or other problems. We must somehow manage to tolerate our grief and yet continue to function effectively. Distress tolerance skills help us to do this.

Linehan (1993) identifies four sets of distress tolerance skills: 1) Distracting with "Wise Mind Accepts"; 2) Self-Soothing; 3) Improving the moment; and 4) Pros and Cons. It should be noted that the skills training manual often uses acronyms to aid the client in remembering skills. One such acronym used to remember distraction skills is "Wise Mind ACCEPTS" which stands for "Activities, Contributing, Comparisons, Emotions, Pushing away, Thoughts, Sensations." These are distraction skills that can aid in tolerating distress and include: 1) Engaging in ACTIVITIES such as walking, cleaning, spending time with a friend; 2) CONTRIBUTING something by volunteering or doing something thoughtful for someone else; 3) COMPARING yourself to people coping as well or less well than you are. Thinking of others less fortunate than you. 4) Seeking out opposite EMOTIONS by reading, watching movies, listening to music, etc; 5) PUSHING away the situation by leaving it mentally for awhile. For example, imagining boxing up the pain and putting it on a shelf temporarily; 6) Focusing on other THOUGHTS such as counting to ten or doing a crossword puzzle; and 7) Focusing on other SENSATIONS such as taking a very hot or very cold shower, eating a mouthful of "pop rocks" candy, or putting your hands in ice cold water.

Improving the moment skills are ways to try to improve the situation at least in your mind. They include using positive imagery, trying to find some meaning, purpose or value in the pain, using prayer or meditation, using relaxation techniques, keeping your mind in the present moment, taking a mental vacation from the situation, and encouraging yourself or getting encouragement from others. The acronym "IMPROVE" is used to help remember these skills and stands for: 1) Imagery; 2) Meaning; 3) Prayer; 4) Relaxation; 5) One thing at a time; 6) take a Vacation; and 7) Encouragment.

Lastly, distress tolerance skills suggest weighing the pros and cons of tolerating the distress versus the pros and cons of not tolerating the distress and instead coping by hurting oneself, abusing chemicals, or some other impulsive behavior. This involves focusing on one's long term goals rather than short term pain relief as well as focusing on the negative consequences of not tolerating the distress.

Another important component of distress tolerance skills is the ability to accept reality. Linehan discusses three important concepts of reality acceptance: 1) Radical Acceptance; 2) Turning the Mind; and 3) Willingness vs. Willfulness. Radical acceptance is a sense of acceptance from deep within. It is acknowledging reality rather than denying or fighting it. Linehan makes an important distinction here between "pain" and "suffering." Pain and distress are seen as a normal part of life which cannot be avoided while "suffering" is seen as a result of the refusal to accept pain.

Turning the mind is the concept of making a choice to accept reality. It involves repeatedly making a commitment to acceptance. A related concept is the difference between willingness and willfulness. Willingness involves listening closely to the wise mind and doing what is needed to be effective in each situation. In contrast, willfulness involves refusing to make needed changes, giving up, trying to fix things or refusing to tolerate the situation.

DIARY CARDS

An important component of skills training is the application of the skills between sessions. To encourage this clients are instructed to use diary cards which list the various skills. Clients are to keep track of any skills they've practiced on the diary card. At the next session, all clients are to share what skills they've tried in the past week. A discussion of how the skills worked and any problems in implementing them ensues. Clients are encouraged to practice all the skills rather than focus on a few. This is encouraged because different skills may work in different situations and the more skills the client has available to them the more likely they are to find one that is effective.

Again, there are detailed instructions for teaching all of these skills in the Skills Training Manual (Linehan, 1993). The skills training group is psychoeducational in nature focusing on the learning of skills. For this reason clients are not allowed to discuss past parasuicidal behavior in the group. The individual therapist then encourages and reinforces the use of the skills.

"CONSULTANT TO THE PATIENT" STRATEGY

Another important DBT concept it the "consultant to patient" strategy. This strategy holds that the therapist does not intervene or consult with others unless the patient is present. Instead the therapist teaches the client how to interact effectively with other treatment providers and the environment. In other words, if a client has a conflict or problem with another provider the therapist will *not* speak to the other staff for the client. Instead, the therapist will discuss how the client can use their interpersonal effectiveness skills in addressing this individual. The exception is when the client does not have the capability or willingness and the immediate outcome is more important than long term learning (e.g. suicide risk). In addition, this does assume that the therapist is participating in the consultation group. This strategy is extremely important for two reasons. First, it reduces the potential for staff splitting. Second, and perhaps even more importantly, it provides an opportunity for the client to practice effective skills.

DEALING WITH PHONE CALLS & EMERGENCIES

Telephone Consultation is particularly important for patients with BPD. Providing between session "coaching" aids in generalization of skills. Telephone consultation reduces the client's sense of alienation when there is a conflict that cannot be addressed until the next session. Telephone consultation when the patient is NOT in crisis helps to alter the pattern of seeking attention in crisis.

Each therapist needs to decide what their own policy will be regarding phone calls, make it clear to the client, and stick with the boundaries set. This will certainly vary depending on one's professional role but in the standard DBT treatment program the telephone consultation is provided by the primary therapist. Certainly the clinician needs to think carefully about their policies based on their personal and professional situation.

Clinicians often express fear or concern about making oneself so available. However, it has been my experience that once the client knows they can call me they rarely abuse this privilege. It is my impression that when phone calls are allowed and even encouraged, the client's abandonment anxieties are significantly relieved and they need to use this option much less often. Utilizing an answering service or separate professional line may aid in limiting direct access to the therapist's home which often provides the therapist with a more tolerable buffer.

I also make it a policy to discuss with clients the appropriate use of phone calls. I advise them that calls taking more than ten minutes are probably beyond these purposes and thus, those issues should be addressed in therapy. I also discuss with them when necessary any abuse or inappropriate use of the phone calls and possible consequences. In that sense, it is handled as a therapy interfering behavior. Finally, and probably most importantly I try to keep myself focused on the purposes of phone consultation and make sure any interactions I have are based on these. In that regard, phone calls should stay focused on one of three purposes: 1) assessing the risk of a parasuicidal client and getting them to the appropriate intervention; 2) coaching them in utilizing their skills to get through a specific situation; and 3) reassurance regarding the relationship.

COMMON PROBLEM CALLERS

Dealing with emergency situations, especially clients with parasuicidal thoughts is often difficult for clinicians. Those working on crisis lines and in emergency rooms have an especially difficult role as they often have to make decisions based on very limited information and often with limited resources. One must err on the side of caution but may also at times take some calculated risks. Again, the reader is referred to Chapter 5 for suggestions for assessing and intervening with clients with parasuicidal ideation.

Additional suggestions for common problem situations are provided here. I would note that this discussion is based on my own clinical experiences and is not necessarily intended to reflect a DBT approach. In conducting workshops and consultation I have found that clinician's consistently ask about four problematic situations which I call the "frequent flyers," the passive resistive client or "yes, butters," the "blackmailer" and the "stuck in the system" client.

"*Frequent flyers*" are clients who repeatedly and consistently use the emergency service system. Unlike clients who make repeated calls while in crisis but at other times make no calls, these clients consistently make repeat calls. It seems they call the minute any hint of distress arises before making any attempts to handle the situation themselves.

A number of strategies may be helpful with such a client. If they are in individual psychotherapy the crisis worker can provide immediate suggestions and then defer further discussion until the therapy session. Frequent nonemergency calls are then discussed in session as a therapy interfering behavior. If they are not in therapy, the crisis worker should strongly encourage therapy and then be careful not to get into conducting phone therapy. Again, the purpose and limits of phone calls will need to be repeatedly emphasized in these clients. Actually setting a time limit for the calls can be helpful and I generally predicate this on the reason that the line has to be kept open for other callers.

If a client seems to call daily or near daily I have found it useful to "schedule" their call. The client is instructed to keep a list of any problems or concerns they have until you call them at a specified time. Having a specified contact will often lessen their anxiety and having them keep a list forces them to practice delaying calling and instead tolerating distress. It has been my experience that when a client does this they eventually no longer need the calls and will terminate them on their own. In addition, it helps the clinician to know when they will be talking to that client and be more mentally prepared. However, it is crucial that if you set up a call you do make it on time. Given you may have other calls it sometimes helps to set a range (e.g. "I'll call sometime between 7 and 7:30).

A similar process works when the client is given a limited number of calls. Again, the client is encouraged to make lists and also to think about whether or not this issue is so important that they want to "use up" a call. Calls should be limited to a number that is somewhat less that the client currently is making and can be progressively limited over time until there is no longer an issue. This is important because if the client is asked to very dramatically decrease their access their anxiety will likely escalate making the problem worse. Thus, a gradual step down process will be better tolerated.

In addition, therapy with these clients should focus on developing distress tolerance skills. It may be useful to work with them regarding delaying the decision to call, identifying how you know if it's really an emergency, and learning other things to try before calling.

"*Yes, butters*" are those clients who call but reject every suggestion you make. No matter what you suggest they say they've tried it or it doesn't work and thus they may as well be dead. This is similar to Linehan's concept of "active passivity" which she defines as "the tendency to approach problems passively and helplessly, rather than actively and determinedly, as well as a corresponding tendency under extreme distress to demand from the environment solutions to life's problems" (Linehan, 1993) It may also be thought of as client who is engaging in willfulness rather than willingness by refusing to accept a situation and insisting someone or something else may change it or they will give up ("I may as well kill myself.") While I would not explain these concepts directly to the client (unless we had already been discussing them in therapy) I would use them to help me understand the behavior and intervene.

One strategy is to use dialectic persuasion to point out the inconsistency in their statements and behavior. In other words I suggest that since they called they must have some hope or some sense that something may be possible. I label this ambivalence and suggest that as long as they are ambivalent they should not do anything irreversible. A helpful question in that regard can be to ask why they have not yet harmed themselves and then reinforce any protective factors identified.

The most effective response I've found with these clients is to ask them "What would you like from me?" Sometimes they say "I just want someone to listen." I then validate their need to be listened to but set a reasonable time limit. Then I use every good listening skill I've ever been taught. I might also suggest a call back or help them identify others who could listen to them.

More often the client will respond, "I don't know." Or "There isn't anything you can do." I then validate this response and suggest that they may simply have to tolerate their distress. We then discuss skills for doing so. Often I will suggest they try tolerating their situation for a specified amount of time and state I will then call back and see how they are doing. If they are still distressed I again suggest tolerance and extend the call back time.

The "*blackmailer*" wants a hospitalization and will say whatever it takes to be admitted. "If you don't admit me I'm going to kill myself." These clients are perhaps most difficult because if you refuse hospitalization they may prove their point, however, if you provide hospitalization it clearly reinforces their tantrum. This places the provider in a "Catch-22" situation that often elicits anger and resentment in the provider. Ultimately the clinician must err on the side of caution while trying various strategies that may break this pattern.

One strategy is to say to the client, "Look, we can always admit you if that's absolutely necessary. I'm just curious what it is that being in the hospital does for you that we can't do on an outpatient basis?" If the client will answer that question it often provides crucial information about what the client needs and you can then assess whether or not you can provide that on an outpatient basis. You can then discuss with the client how that need can be met and encourage them to try to outpatient option first emphasizing that hospitalization is always an option if it doesn't work. I also try to discuss with the client disadvantages of hospitalization that may deter them such as cost, inability to smoke, inability to come and go as you please, etc.

An important factor in this situation is the client's need for control. Clearly making such a threat is an attempt to gain control of the decision (i.e. "If you don't do what I want I'm going to punish you."). Thus, throughout the interventions the client's sense of control should be maintained and enhanced. That is why it is so important to emphasize that hospitalization is an option but to try to give them other options as well. Any time you can allow them choices this will aid in establishing control.

Often these clients are highly anxious and agitated and see hospitalization as the only means for controlling or relieving their anxiety. Sometimes they will accept other options such as, "You can always be admitted if you need to but what if we try having you take your medication and wait here and rest for an hour to see if you're feeling any better."

Finally, if at all possible try to identify and eliminate any secondary gains from hospitalization. In that regard inpatient staff should try to make hospital stays less pleasant for clients who have this pattern. This should not be confused with "punishing" the client for their behavior but rather by insisting that the client work on issues while hospitalized and minimizing nurturance when threats are made. Some hospitals address this by threatening commitment or state hospitalization if a client repeatedly comes in under these circumstances. While this can sometimes work it is an expensive solution and may actually backfire with further dependence.

Often related to these secondary gains from hospitalization are systemic issues. Such systemic issues also define the "*stuck in the system*" client. These are clients who seek emergency services due to systemic issues which may be completely unrelated. For example, while doing my internship at the Veteran's Hospital we would often see alcoholic or homeless clients come in the third or fourth week of the month only to "feel much better" the first of the month. The reality was they got their pension or disability check on the first and had money for liquor and/or housing then they would become suicidal the same time the following month when they ran out of money.

Other clients may not have insurance coverage for medications but can get their medications paid for as part of their hospitalization so they get suicidal when they need their meds. Sometimes this manipulation is conscious and sometimes it is not. Regardless, this behavior is unlikely to change unless the system that reinforces it does. In that regard, the best the clinician can do is to try to identify any systemic issues that may reinforce this pattern, use creative problem solving to try to address these issues, work to change the system, and then practice distress tolerance skills to accept a less than perfect world!

CHAPTER SUMMARY

Clinical trials support the use of DBT with clients who have BPD yet many clinicians are not familiar with the model. Developed by Dr. Marsha Linehan, DBT draws from a foundation in cognitive behavioral therapy and incorporates concepts from Buddhist teachings and dialectic philosophy. DBT is both a principle and protocol driven approach which integrates both acceptance and change strategies.

While concepts from DBT can be applied in a variety of settings the standard DBT treatment model consists of individual psychotherapy, group skills training, telephone consultation, and the therapist's consultation group. The skills training group is psychoeducational in nature and focuses on four skills training modules including: 1) mindfulness skills; 2) emotion regulation skills; 3) interpersonal effectiveness skills and 4) distress tolerance skills. Diary cards are utilized to keep track of between session practice and aid in a discussion of skills at each group.

The therapist acts as a consultant to the patient, encouraging them to practice their skills in interactions with others rather than directly intervening. Clients are encouraged to call the therapist in between session for coaching in applying their skills or reassurance regarding the relationship. While that vast majority of clients do not abuse this privilege, clients do on occasion use emergency services inappropriately. It is recommended that this be approached as a therapy interfering behavior with a focus on developing alternative solutions whenever possible.

8

Understanding the Clinician's Struggle

RECOGNIZING COUNTERTRANSFERENCE

As already discussed the Borderline client's pattern of interacting can be especially likely to elicit strong emotional reactions in others. For this reason clinicians must be especially vigilant to countertransference issues. Our reactions to clients can give us important information about the client's needs and issues but they can also lead us to act in nonhelpful and even damaging ways.

One helpful rule of thumb for recognizing countertransference is to be aware of changes from your "usual practice." In other words, ask yourself if this is something you typically do with clients. That is not to say you may not make exceptions but these should be carefully thought out. Before doing something different from what you usually do, get consultation. Carefully consider the therapeutic and ethical implications of altering your practice before proceeding. After consideration, you may decide on a usual course of action, but then you must document your decision making and why you're doing something out of the ordinary.

For example, I do not usually have lunch with my clients. However, if I were working with an anorexic client around her anxiety at mealtime I may actually put it in the treatment plan to bring lunch into session or go out to lunch in order to complete in vivo exposure. This would be staffed and the reasons for doing so as well as potential risks would be carefully documented in the treatment plan.

In addition, I do not usually yell and point my finger at clients in our sessions. Yet, I am embarrassed to admit that in a consultation with a Borderline client I found myself doing just that! Fortunately, I immediately recognized my inappropriate behavior, consciously lowered the volume of my voice, and literally sat on my hands. I realized that our interaction was triggering my issues which were already surfacing due to other issues that day. Countertransference was leading me to act in ways that are not commonly part of my practice. I needed to alter my behavior and separate my issues from the immediate issue with the client. In this case, feelings of inadequacy and incompetence, common countertransference issues with borderlines were influencing my behavior.

There are two other issues I find especially dangerous in working with clients with BPD both for myself and for other clinicians. There are most certainly others but these occur with enough frequency to warrant discussion. These include the therapists "rescue fantasies" and the "total responsibility vs. complete uselessness dialectic."

RESCUE FANTASIES

We become caregivers for many reasons but certainly a desire to help others is clearly one important factor. Unfortunately, many of us enter these professions with unresolved issues of our own that get played out in our professional interactions. In particular, most of us have at one time or another had some form or "rescue fantasy." Perhaps this stems from a need to be needed or to correct some issue in our life where no one rescued us. Regardless, this fantasy is especially counterproductive in dealing with clients with BPD.

Because Borderline clients have a tendency toward active passivity and are truly very wounded and damaged people they elicit in us our desire to save them. We want to be the one to save them from their horrible lives. How frustrating it is then when our efforts are not sufficient to eliminate their suffering or when, worse yet, they refuse or resent our help. In particular we become angry and resentful when we save the client from their own self-injurious impulses and yet they continue them.

We cannot save the Borderline client. To think we can is arrogant and self-defeating. Further, it takes away the clients autonomy. *Borderline clients need to save themselves*. The best we can do is to help provide them with the hope and skills to do so. Acceptance of this reality and an awareness of our rescue fantasies are critical in working with clients with BPD.

THE TOTAL RESPONSIBILITY VS. COMPLETE USELESSNESS DIALECTIC

Because of our desire to rescue the Borderline client and our inability to do so we can become caught in what I refer to as "The Total Responsibility vs. Complete Uselessness Dialectic." We may vacillate between feeling completely responsible for the client's well being and feeling completely inadequate and useless. In addition, clients may vacillate in their perceptions of us based on this polarity. Thus, at one point they helpless ask us to make all decisions for them and at other times insist "you can't help me," or "therapy is stupid." Our temptation then is to be over active in our role with the client or to give up completely, often saying they're "untreatable" or abruptly referring them to another therapist. Again, neither is a helpful response.

We must resolve this dialectic in our own minds and behavior by assuming we can be helpful but refusing to be completely responsible. This is a constant balancing act between active intervention and insisting on client responsibility. We must not fall prey to thinking we are inadequate. Certainly we may benefit from further training or consultation but ultimately it is our persistence and tenacity that often pays off with these clients in the long run.

ABOUT SPLITTING

The concept of splitting is so common in the discussion of clients with BPD it would be remiss not to address it in this text. This is particularly an issue in inpatient or residential settings where multiple providers or varying backgrounds are involved with the client. Again, it should be emphasized that adopting a consultant to patient approach will greatly reduce the effects of splitting.

Too often however, splitting is erroneously interpreted to be a client's conscious attempt to turn people against each other or create chaos. While this is perhaps true at times I would argue that clients most often do *not* engage in splitting with conscious or malicious intentions. Instead, in keeping with dialectic philosophy, splitting behavior likely occurs because of a failure of dialectic resolution.

In fact, Linehan offers a novel definition of splitting. She states that splitting occurs "when the staff cannot agree on how to treat the patient." Notice the change in where the responsibility for resolving the split lies. In fact, that is often what happens. One staff thinks a client's behavior should be ignored or punished while another staff thinks the client needs more nurturance or support. In reality, there is probably some truth in both positions.

My suggestion to you is that the next time you experience "staff splitting" you think of it as a dialectic failure. Listen to both staff opinions. Look for the "kernel of truth" in each position and for what they have in common. This information will likely help you resolve the tension between opposite approaches and come up with a more balanced and useful approach.

CHANGING UNHELPFUL THOUGHTS

As is evident throughout this text I believe that one of the greatest impediments to effectively treating clients with BPD is our own negative and often erroneous beliefs about them. As such, it is my opinion that the most effective change we can make is to learn to alter our own thinking in ways that reduce our frustration and ultimately increase our effectiveness. Hopefully the information provided in this text is helpful in better understanding these clients and thus, changing negative thinking.

In addition I encourage professional to use cognitive behavior techniques to evaluate and change their thinking throughout the treatment process. If you find yourself feeling frustrated or stuck with a client look at your own thoughts. Ask yourself, "Is that really true?" and "Even if it is true is it helpful to think that?" If the answer to either question is "no" you need to engage in thought replacement. Some common unhelpful thoughts and possible replacement thoughts are summarized in Table 13.

Table 13: Common Unhelpful Thoughts and Alternatives

- *"I'll get sued if my client commits suicide."*—Anyone can sue me for anything at anytime. Did I provide a reasonable standard of care?
- *"If my client commits suicide it is my fault."*—Clients make the choice whether or not to commit suicide. Did I provide a reasonable standard of care?
- *"She is being manipulative. She is intentionally . . ."* Her behavior is an attempt to regulate emotions. How can I help her better do that? What does she need?
- *"She doesn't want to get better."*—She wants to get better but doesn't know how.

- *"She should realize and appreciate what I do for her. She should realize how her behavior affects me."*—I need to get my need for recognition met elsewhere.
- "She is selfish and insensitive."—*What's wrong with that? What is she needing that is so important?*

In addition, when trying to understand borderline behavior, use the "arrow down" technique to arrive at the fundamental problem before intervening. In cognitive therapy the arrow down technique is a process by which one identifies their thought then repeatedly asks themselves "What would that mean?" until one arrives at the underlying basic belief. For example, instead of stopping at "she's doing that for attention" ask further questions until the fundamental problem is identified. This is described in Table 14.

Table 14: Sample Arrow Down Technique

She's doing it for attention.

What would that mean?

She needs attention.

What's wrong with that?

Nothing. Everyone needs attention sometimes.
But it's the way she's doing it.

What's wrong with that?

It's indirect. It doesn't take others into account.

What would that mean?

Either she needs it so bad that she's will to sacrifice others feelings
or she doesn't know how else to do it.

What would that mean

We need to find other ways to meet that need or
to tolerate it being unmet.

(etc.)

PREVENTING BURNOUT

Such changes in thinking are a primary weapon against clinical burnout with these clients. If you use theory to understand BPD behavior instead of personalizing it or assuming the client is being "manipulative" you will be well on your way to effective interventions. As importantly, you will find yourself less frustrated and fatigued.

In addition, clinicians should minimize the number of Borderline clients on their caseload. If you cannot limit the number of clients you will need to set realistic limits about what you can do for each client. In that regard it can be very helpful to ask yourself "What is my role?" and "What is most important to do first?" Role clarification and priority setting is critical in the treatment of clients with BPD. These clients come in with multiple problems and are so labile it is easy to feel overwhelmed or be distracted. Continually focusing on your role, setting priorities, and sticking with a goal until it is completed with increase your sense of focus and likely your success.

These questions are especially important for inpatient and crisis clinicians. These clinicians often see clients in crisis, thus reinforcing the perception that the clients don't get better. The fact is, when they are better, you don't see them! Dealing with clients in extreme situations is especially stressful and thus, self care is crucial. Focusing on immediate crisis intervention and coordinating the longer term issues with the outpatient treatment provider is crucial.

These are demanding clients where change can be painstakingly slow. For that reason it is crucial that clinicians working with Borderlines get a great deal of support. I cannot emphasize enough the importance of consultations and/or supervision in that regard. Part of the role of the consultant and supervisor is to serve as a "cheerleader" for the clinician. While the clinician continuously supports and encourages the client, the supervision or consultation team continuously supports and encourages the clinician. Clinicians, like clients, need to hear what they are doing well and that they are appreciated. Clients are too overwhelmed with their own needs to meet this need in the therapist. Thus, supervision and consultation is a necessity.

CHAPTER SUMMARY

Because clients with BPD are especially difficult to work with it is critical that the clinician practice good self care. Clinicians should be especially vigilant for countertransference issues which can often be evident when the clinician does something outside their usual mode of practicing. Clinicians must also be aware of their own rescues fantasies as well as the tension between wanting to be all powerful and feeling completely useless. When splitting occurs clinicians must recognize this as a dialectic failure and work to identify the two opposing views and the truth in each. Assuming the client has malicious intent is likely untrue and most often unhelpful. Instead the clinician should identify their own negative thoughts and use the arrow down technique to identify the underlying problem. The clinician must also be clear about their role and set priorities.

All of these issues can be addressed though the process of supervision and/or consultation. Consultation is critical to even the most experience clinician when working with clients with BPD. The consultation group can help the clinician see ineffective patterns as well as serving as support and "cheerleaders" in the sometimes slow and arduous process of treating clients with BPD.

9

Redefining Success

Life certainly can be a struggle for the client with BPD and those around her but it must be remembered that no one chooses this struggle. Borderlines do not wake up in the morning and plot how to make life difficult for everyone. They wake up to a life that is difficult and lack the skills to cope effectively. By understanding the etiology and dynamics of this disorder both the client and those attempting to help her may be more effective. Both must change their unhelpful thoughts and behaviors into ones that are productive and effective. And both may have to redefine what they consider "success."

REDEFINING SUCCESS FOR THE CLIENT

Clients often give up because they cannot do what they expect themselves to do or what they see others do with ease. As previously noted, part of what happens in an invalidating environment is that they learn to set unrealistic goals for themselves. Other clients see themselves as so incapable that they refuse to set goals at all. Part of the therapeutic task may be to redefine what success would mean and to set priorities. I believe three concepts are critical in defining "success" for the person with BPD: 1) Survival; 2) Progress Not Perfection; and 3) A Life Worth Living.

Borderline clients have often survived very difficult life circumstances. They are indeed survivors. Yet for many the most difficult survival task is resisting their own parasuicidal tendencies. Day to day survival is the most critical goal for clients with BPD. They have to live through each day in order to have any chance at all for other changes to happen.

For this reason, the DBT approach targets the elimination of parasuicidal behavior as the number one priority in treatment.

Linehan recommends making a commitment to stop parasuicidal behavior as part of the initial treatment agreement. I tell clients very clearly, "I cannot help you if you are dead so our number one priority is to keep you alive." For the Borderline client with strong parasuicidal tendencies, every day she stays alive is a success. If she can stay alive long enough, odds are that things will improve significantly.

"Progress not Perfection" is an old Alcoholics Anonymous slogan that is especially pertinent for clients with BPD. Too often these clients will give up before even trying something, or will try something but give up because they couldn't do it perfectly. Clinicians must help clients to see their progress. A change in the right direction, no matter how small, is a success. The client who makes a phone call before engaging in parasuicidal behavior when she has not done so in the past has experienced success. In other words, success is defined by each step in the right directions not in whether or not one gets to their final destination.

Finally, while certainly the client who stops self injurious behavior is "successful," this alone should not define success. The overarching goal of DBT is "a life worth living." This suggests that success is not just defined by the elimination of problem behaviors. Success is defined by the client achieving the things in life that give the client a sense of satisfaction, meaning, and purpose. The client must learn not only to tolerate distress but also what brings them joy and pleasure. If the client and clinician will focus on this goal as well often many problematic behaviors will eliminate themselves.

REDEFINING SUCCESS FOR THE CLINICIAN

Just as clients need to redefine their notion of success so too do the clinicians working with clients with BPD. Again, this disorder may be considered a chronic disorder where the goal becomes effective management not cure. Too often clinicians, like Borderline client's themselves, give up when they do not see the changes they believe "should" happen. They blame the client or blame themselves, engaging in an unhelpful dialectic failure. Thus, clinicians may need to redefine success in ways that are more productive. I believe four concepts are helpful in redefining "success" for the clinician: 1) Damage Control 2) Patience and Persistence; and 3) Continual Assessment/Continual Learning; 4) Work worth Doing.

Like the Borderline client who sometimes must focus solely on survival, so too the clinician at times must focus solely on damage control. When I am feeling helpless or ineffective in my work I sometimes change my focus from "How can I make this better?" to "How can I keep this from getting any worse?" Much like a firefighter who has learned that he or she cannot put out every fire and some times must simply "contain" the fire, I focus on damage control. I stop trying to control the situation and instead try to find ways that I can redirect things to a safer or more positive course. There are moments where damage control is the best you can do.

At the same time however, I believe fervently that if I can do this long enough "the fire will die out" and things will get better. Patience and persistence are critical components to the successful work with clients with BPD. Too often caregivers get frustrated and give up on these clients which only reinforces their abandonment fears and destructive patterns. Remember if you can hang in there long enough the odds are in your favor.

This is not to imply that you simply "put up with anything." Clearly clinicians must set clear boundaries but they must also believe in the effectiveness of the work. If you do not, how can your client possibly have any faith? A careful distinction should be made here that this doesn't mean the caregiver "will always be there." It is a commitment that "I will be there whenever and however I can be and I believe even when I can't be there the client has the abilities to get well." Believe in the patience and persistence of yourself and your client.

Continuous assessment and learning is critical in the treatment of clients with BPD. Too often clinicians do an assessment, think they know what to do, and give up if it doesn't work. Working with Borderline clients is a continuous process of assessing, intervening, and reassessing. It means constantly reviewing what is working and what isn't, whether or not you've tried it long enough, and what else may work. Each client is different requiring a unique and individualized response. To be successful with Borderlines you must keep reassessing the situation.

In addition, you must keep learning. There is no one "right" thing to do or "right" way of doing things. Even experienced clinicians can learn from new approaches or a review of theory. Don't give up if you don't learn every DBT concept the first time. Focus on a few and when you've mastered them move on to some new ones. Just as clients have to work at skills training so do clinicians.

Finally, regardless of the changes a client may or may not make, the successful clinician will make this "Work Worth Doing." The successful clinician will seek meaning in their work and learn to see value in it, irrespective of the client's progress. They will set their own goals and focus on their own progress in applying therapeutic approaches. We cannot allow the client's success or lack thereof to define our own success. Frankly, by simply sticking with it, you will have already done better than many clinicians.

I hope this book has given you some new ways of looking at these clients and new ideas for intervening. For me, this was a work worth doing, because it serves as a reminder to me as to why these clients are the way they are and why I do what I do. This understanding keeps me positive and fresh in my clinical work.

Working with Borderlines can be a struggle, but it can also be rewarding beyond belief. We have an opportunity to literally save lives and to help individuals make those lives worth living. In my book, that is truly work worth doing! That is succeeding.

Appendix A

50 THINGS YOU CAN TRY INSTEAD OF HURTING YOURSELF

(**Note:** While some of these may sound strange, any activity that refocuses your attention and delays the impulse to injure is likely to help you through the crisis long enough so that your body can self regulate. All of these things have been used by others in the past and found to work for some people. You will feel better. You just have to hang on long enough!)

1. Talk to someone.
2. Delay your decision for (5) minutes.
3. Hold an ice cube in each hand for 10 minutes.
4. Put your hands in a bucket of ice water for five minutes.
5. Go for a walk or run for a half hour.
6. Take a nap.
7. Take a bath.
8. Take a hot or cold shower.
9. Have (safe) sex.
10. Yell, scream or cry.
11. Play favorite music loudly.
12. Sing *very* loudly.
13. Focus on your presence in the room.
14. Practice Mindfulness
15. Pound on your bed until exhausted.
16. Practice thought stopping.
17. Put a rubber band around your wrist and snap it.
18. Make lists (reasons to get better, positives . . .)

19. Throw tomatoes at a tree.
20. Mark your arm with red lipstick.
21. Masturbate.
22. Tear up newspapers or phone books.
23. Mark your arm with red or black magic marker.
24. Draw a picture on yourself.
25. Give yourself a Henna Tattoo.
26. Write/read a list of reasons you don't like hurting yourself.
27. Write/read a list of positive affirmations.
28. Call your therapist.
29. Draw a picture.
30. Write a letter.
31. Play a computer game.
32. Call a crisis line.
33. Watch cartoons or a favorite movie.
34. Knit, crochet, needlepoint or some other focused physical activity.
35. Paint
36. Watch fish in a tank for 20 minutes.
37. Practice relaxation techniques.
38. Make paper clip chains.
39. Wash dishes (even if they're already clean).
40. Pray.
41. Meditate.
42. Knead bread dough (or play dough), roll out dough or pie crust, or crush graham crackers with a rolling pin.
43. Smudge (or burn incense).
44. Play with a pet.
45. Watch your favorite video.
46. Find a playground and swing as high as you can.
47. Beat a drum for 10 minutes. (or play another musical instrument if you know how)
48. Hold a stuffed animal or pet.
49. Count things (ceiling tiles, colors, etc.)
50. Lie upside down on a chair or staircase for 30 seconds to one minute.

Appendix B: Risk Assessment Worksheet

SUICIDE/VIOLENCE ASSESSMENT & INTERVENTION WORKSHEET

Assessment of Risk Factors:

Frequency/Intensity of Thoughts of Death: ____________________

Frequency/Intensity of Ideation: ____________________

Plan: ___ none ____________________

Means: ___ none ____________________

Time/Place: ___ none ____________________

Intended Victim: ___ none ____________________

Intent: Syntonic Dystonic Weak Moderate Strong

Prior Attempts: ___ none

___ within past 3 months

___ within last year

Date of last attempt: ____________________

Prior Hospitalizations: ___ none Dates: ______________________

Family/Social History: ___ none ______________________

Behavioral Indicators: ___ none ______________________

Altered Mental State: ___ none ______________________

Alcohol/Drug Use: ___ none ______________________

Other Risk Factors: ___ none ______________________

____

____

____

Assessment of Protective Factors:

Support System: ______________________

Protective Beliefs: ______________________

Fears/Responsibility: ______________________

Strong Alliance: ______________________

History of Resource Use: ______________________

Other: ______________________

Recommended Interventions:

___ Continue to verbally monitor until ______________________

___ Specific monitor w/ frequency ______________________

___ Client contracted with therapist. Duration: ______________

___ Client informed of emergency procedures.

___ Contacted collateral support: ______________________

___ Removal of firearms or other means.

___ Increase session frequency to ______________________

___ Referred for further assessment to ______________________

___ Voluntary Hospitalization.

___ Involuntary Hospitalization.

Client's Response to Intervention:

___ Agreed/Complied ___ Actively Declined

Notes: ____

____

____

____

____

Resources

RECOMMENDED READING:

Alderman, Tracy (1997). *The Scarred Soul: Understanding and Ending Self-Inflicted Violence.* New Harbinger Publications, Oakland, CA.

Cohen, R. H. (1997). *The Angry Heart: Overcoming Borderline and Addictive Disorders.* New Harbinger Publications, Oakland, CA.

Dimeff, L. & Linehan, M. M. (2001) Dialectical behavior therapy in a nutshell. *The California Psychologist, 34,* 10–13. (available at www.behavioraltech.org)

Kreger, R. (2002). *The Stop Walking On Eggshells Workbook.* Oakland, CA. New Harbinger Publications.

Kreisman, J. J. & Straus, H. (1989) *I Hate You—Don't Leave Me: Understanding the Borderline Personality Disorder.* Avon Books, New York.

Lawson, C. A. (2002). *Understanding the Borderline Mother: Helping Her Children Transcend the Intense, Unpredictable, and Volatile Relationship.* Northvale, NJ. Jason Aronson Inc.

Mason, P. T. & Kreger, R. (1998). *Stop Walking On Eggshells: Taking Your Life Back When Someone You Care About Has Borderline Personality Disorder.* Oakland, CA. New Harbinger Publications.

Thorton, M. F. (1998). *Eclipses: Behind the Borderline Personality Disorder.* Monte Sano Publishing, Madison, AL.

VIDEOS:

Linehan, M. M. (2000) *DBT Skills Training Video: Opposite Action.* Seattle, WA. The Behavioral Technology Transfer Group.

Linehan, M. M. (1995). *Treating Borderline Personality Disorder: The Dialectical Approach.* New York. The Guilford Press.

Linehan, M. M. (1995). *Understanding Borderline Personality Disorder: The Dialectical Approach.* New York. The Guilford Press.

INTERNET SITES:

www.pesihealthcare.com

www.behavioraltech.com

www.BPDCentral.com

www.onelist.com/subscribe.cgi/WelcometoOz

www.mhsanctuary.com/borderline

www.ruinyourlife.com (regarding self-mutilation)

TO CONTACT THE AUTHOR:

drcolleen@charter.net

References

Ajamieh, A. & Ansseau, M. (2000). Biological markers in schizotypal and borderline personality disorders. *Encephale, 26*(6), 42–54.

American Psychiatric Association (1998). Integrating DBT into Community Mental Health: The Mental Health Center of Greater Manchester, New Hampshire. *Psychiatric Services, 49,* 1338–1340.

American Psychiatric Association. (2001). Part A: Treatment Recommendations for Patients with Borderline Personality Disorder. *American Journal of Psychiatry, 158*(10), 5–25.

Antai-Otong, D. (2001). *Psychiatric Emergencies: How to accurately assess and manage the patient in crisis.* Eau Claire, WI: PESI Healthcare.

Arntz, A., van den Hoorn, M., Cornelia, J., Verheul, R., van den Bosch, W. M., de Bie, A. J. (2003). Reliability and validity of the borderline personality disorder severity index. *Journal of Personality Disorders, 17*(1), 45–59.

Bateman, A. & Fonagy, P. (2003). Health service utilization costs for borderline personality disorder patients treated with psychoanalytically oriented partial hospitalization versus general psychiatric care. *American Journal of Psychiatry, 160*(1), 169–171.

Coccaro, E. F. & Kavoussi, R. J. (1991). Biological and pharmacological aspects of borderline personality disorder. *Hospital and Community Psychiatry, 42*(10), 1029–1033.

Cleary, M. Siegfried, N. & Walter, G. (2002) Experience, knowledge and attitudes of mental health staff regarding clients with a borderline personality disorder. *International Journal of Mental Health Nursing, 11*(3), 186–191.

Dean, M. A. (2001). *Borderline Personality Disorder: The Latest Assessment and Treatment Strategies.* Kansas City: Compact Clinicals.

Dimeff, L., Koerner, K. & Linehan, M. M. (2001). *Summary of Research on DBT.* The Behavioral Technology Transfer Group. Seattle, WA 98105.

Favazza, A. R. & Coterio, K. (1989). Female habitual self-mutilators. *Acta Psychiatrica Scandinavica, 79*, 783–289.

Fine, M. E. & Sansone, R. A. (1990). Dilemmas in the management of suicidal behavior individuals with Borderline Personality Disorder. *American Journal of Psychotherapy, 44*(2), 160–172.

Gartner, J., Hurt, S. W., Gartner, A. (1989) Psychological test signs of borderline personality disorder: A review of the empirical literature. *Journal of Personality Assessment, 54*(3), 423–441.

Goin, M. K. (1998). Borderline personality disorder: Splitting countertransference, *15*(11).

Goldstein, W. N. (1998) The Borderline Patient: An Overview. *Psychiatric Times,* January, 1998.

Galloway, V. A. & Brodsky, S. L. (2003) Caring less, doing more: The role of therapeutic detachment with volatile and unmotivated clients. *America Journal of Psychotherapy, 57*(1), 32–38.

Grilo, C. M., Sanislow, C. A., Skodal, A. E., Gunderson, J. G. & Stout, R. L. (2003). Do eating disorders co-occur with personality disorders? Comparison groups matter. *International Journal of Eating Disorders, 33*(2), 155–164.

Guzder, J., Paris, J., Zelkowitz, P., & Feldman, R. (1999). Psychological Risk Factors for Borderline Pathology in School Age Children. *Journal of the American Academy of Child & Adolescent Psychiatry, 38*(2), 206–212.

Jeungling, F. D., Schmahl, C., Heblinger, B., Ebert, D., Bremner, J. ., Gostomzyk, J., Bohus, M., Lieb, K. Positron emission tomography in female patients with borderline personality disorder. *Journal of Psychiatric Research, 37*(2), 109–115.

Judd, P. H. & Ruff, R. M. (1993). Neuropsychological Dysfunction in Borderline Personality Disorder. *Journal of Personality Disorders, 7*(4), 275–284.

Keperman, I., Russ, M. J., & Shearin, E. (1997). Self-injurious behavior and mood regulation in Borderline patients. *Journal of Personality Disorders, 11*(2), 146–157.

Kernberg, O., Koenigsberg, H., Stone, M., Yeomans, F., Appelbaun, A. & Diamond, D. (2002). *Borderline Patients: Extending the Limits of Treatability.* New York: Basic Books.

Koenigsberg, H. W. (1984). Indications for hospitalization in the treatment of borderline patients. *Psychiatric Quarterly, 56*(4), 247–258.

La Rowe, K. D. (2001) *Working with Survivors of Traumatic Stress.* Eau Claire, WI: PESI Healthcare, LLC.

Leichsenring, F. (1999). Development and First Results of the Borderline Personality Inventory: A Self-Report Instrument for Assessing Borderline Personality Organization. *Journal of Personality Assessment, 73*(1), 45–63.

Levine, D., Marziali, E., & Hood, J. (1997). Emotional processing in Borderline Personality Disorders. *Journal of Nervous and Mental Disease, 185,* 240–246.

Linehan, M. M. (1993) *Cognitive-Behavioral Treatment of Borderline Personality Disorder.* New York: The Guilford Press.

Linehan, M. M. (1993) *Skills Training Manual for Treating Borderline Personality Disorder.* New York: The Guilford Press.

Miller, L. J. (1989). Inpatient management of borderline personality disorder. *Journal of Personality Disorders, 3*(2), 122–134.

Millon, T. (1981) *Disorders of Personality: DSM-III, Axis II.* New York: John Wiley & Sons.

Morey, L. C. (1991). *Personality Assessment Inventory.* Odessa, FL: Psychological Assessment Resources, or San Antonio, TX: The Psychological Corporation.

Paris, J. (1990). Completed suicide in borderline personality disorder. *Psychiatric Annals, 20*(1), 19–21.

Paris, J. (2002). Implications of long-term outcome research for the management of patients with borderline personality disorder. *Harvard Review of Psychiatry, 10*(6), 315–323.

Paris, J., Brown, R., & Nowlis, D. (1987). Long-term Follow-up of Borderline Patients in a General Hospital. *Comprehensive Psychiatry, 28*(6), 530–535.

Plakun, E. M. (1991). Prediction of Outcome in Borderline Personality Disorder. *Journal of Personality Disorders, 5*(2), 92–101.

Sar, V., Kundakci, T., et al (2003). The Axis-I dissociative disorder comorbidity of borderline personality disorder among psychiatric outpatients. *Journal of Trauma & Dissociation, 4*(1), 199–136.

Schmahl, C. G., Vermetten, E. Elzinga, B. M., Bremner, J.D. (2003). Magnetic resonance imaging of hippocampal and amygdala volume in women with childhood abuse and borderline personality disorder. *Psychiatry Research. Neuroimaging, 122*(3), 193–198.

Schroeder, S. R., Oster-Granite, M. L., & Thompson, T. (2002). *Self Injurious Behavior: Gene, Brain, Behavior Relationships.* Washington, DC. American Psychological Association.

Siever, L. J. (1997). The biology of borderline Personality Disorder. *The Journal of the California Alliance for the Mentally Ill.*

Soloff, P. H. (1994). Is there any drug treatment of choice for the borderline patient? *Acta Psychiatrica Scandinavica, 89*(379), 50–55.

Soloff, P. H. (2000). Psychopharmacology of Borderline Personality Disorder. *Psychiatric Clinics of North America, 23*(1), 169–92.

Spitzer, R. L., Williams, J. B. W., & Gibbon, M. (1987) *Structured Clinical Interview for DSM-III-R.* New York: New York State Psychiatric Institute.

Stone, M. H., Hurt, S. W., and Stone, D. K. (1987). The PI 500: Long-Term Follow-up of Borderline Inpatients Meeting DSM-III Criteria I. Global Outcome. *Journal of Personality Disorders, 1*(4), 291–298.

Swartz, M. Blazer, D., George, L. & Winfield, I. (1990). Estimating the prevalence of borderline personality disorder in the community. *Journal of Personality Disorders, 4*(3), 257–272.

White, C. N., Gunderson, J. G., Zanarini, M. C., Hudson, J. I. (2003). Family studies of borderline personality disorder: A review. *Harvard Review of Psychiatry, 11*(1), 8–19.

Zanarini, M. C. (1997). Pathways to the development of borderline personality disorder. *Journal of Personality Disorders, 11*(1), 93–104.

Zanarini, M. C. (2003). The longitudinal course of borderline psychopathology: 6-year prospective follow-up of the phenomenology of borderline personality disorder. *American Journal of Psychiatry, 160*(2), 274–283.

Zanarini, M. C. & Frankenburg, F. R. (2003). Omega-3 fatty acid treatment of women with borderline personality disorder. A double-blind, placebo-controlled pilot study. *American Journal of Psychiatry, 160*(1), 167–169.

Zanarini, M. C., Frankenburg, F. R., Dubo, E. D., Sickel, A. E., Trikna, A. N., Levin, A. & Reynolds, V. (1998). Axis I Comorbidity of Borderline Personality Disorder. *American Journal of Psychiatry, 155*(12), 1733–1739.

Zanarini, M. C., Gunderson, J. G., Frankenburg, F. R., & Chauncey, D. L. (1989). The revised diagnostic interview for borderlines: Discriminating BPD from other Axis II disorders. *Journal of Personality Disorders, 3*(1), 10–18.

Zanarini, M. C., Frankenburg, F. R., Reich, D. B., Marion, M. F., Haynes, M. C. & Gunderson, J. G. (1999)..Violence in the lives of adult borderline patients. *Journal of Nervous and Mental Disease, 187*(2), 65–71.

Zelkowitz, P., Paris, J., Guzder, J., & Feldman, R. (2001). Diatheses and stressors in borderline pathology of childhood: the role of neuropsychological risk and trauma. *Journal of American Academy of Child and Adolescent Psychiatry, 40*(1), 100–105.

STUDY PACKAGE
CONTINUING EDUCATION CREDIT INFORMATION

BORDERLINE PERSONALITY DISORDER
STRUGGLING, UNDERSTANDING, SUCCEEDING

Thank you for choosing PESI Healthcare as your continuing education provider. Our goal is to provide you with current, accurate and practical information from the most experienced and knowledgeable speakers and authors.

Listed below are the continuing education credit(s) currently available for this self-study package. ***Please note, your state licensing board dictates whether self study is an acceptable form of continuing education. Please refer to your state rules and regulations.*

Counselors: PESI HealthCare, LLC is recognized by the National Board for Certified Counselors to offer continuing education for National Certified Counselors. Provider #: 5896. We adhere to NBCC Continuing Education Guidelines. These self-study materials qualify for 3.0 contact hours.

Psychologists: PESI is approved by the American Psychological Association to offer continuing education for psychologists. PESI maintains responsibility for the material. PESI is offering this self-study activity for 3.0 hours of continuing education credit.

Social Workers: PESI HealthCare, 1030, is approved as a provider for social work continuing education by the Association of Social Work Boards (ASWB), (540-829-6880) through the Approved Continuing Education (ACE) program. Licensed Social Workers should contact their individual state boards to determine self-study approval and to review continuing education requirements for licensure renewal. Social Workers will receive 3.0 continuing education clock hours for completing this self-study material.

Addiction Counselors: PESI HealthCare, LLC is a Provider approved by NAADAC Approved Education Provider Program. Provider #: 366. These self-study materials qualify for 3.5 contact hours.

Nurses: PESI HealthCare, LLC, Eau Claire is an approved provider of continuing nursing education by the Wisconsin Nurses Association Continuing Education Approval Program Committee, an accredited approver by the American Nurses Credentialing Center's Commission on Accreditation. This approval is accepted and/or recognized by all state nurses associations that adhere to the ANA criteria for accreditation. This learner directed educational activity qualifies for 3.5 contact hours. PESI Healthcare certification: CA #06538.

Procedures:
1. Read book.
2. Complete the post-test/evaluation form and mail it along with payment to the address on the form.

Your completed test/evaluation will be graded. If you receive a passing score (80% and above), you will be mailed a certificate of successful completion with earned continuing education credits. If you do not pass the post-test, you will be sent a letter indicating areas of deficiency, references to the appropriate sections of the manual for review and your post-test. The post-test must be resubmitted and receive a passing grade before credit can be awarded.

If you have any questions, please feel free to contact our customer service department at 1-800-843-7763.

844-8260

PESI HealthCare, LLC
200 SPRING ST. STE B, P.O. BOX 1000
EAU CLAIRE, WI 54702-1000

Product Number: ZHS008540 **CE Release Date:** 03/02/04